COLLINS MATHS DICTIONARY

Second Edition

Kay Gardner

Collins Educational
An imprint of HarperCollinsPublishers

© 1984 Kay Gardner
First impression 1984 Second edition 1985
Reprinted 1989, 1991, 1992, 1993, 1995, 1996, 1997.
Reprinted 1998 (twice), 1999 (twice), 2000

Designed and illustrated
by Jeff Carter and Patricia Bernaudin
Typeset by Tradespools Limited, Frome, Somerset
Printed by Scotprint

www.CollinsEducation.com
On-line support for schools and colleges

ISBN 0 00 315341 X schools
     0 00 197092 5 trade

Collins Educational
An imprint of HarperCollinsPublishers
77–85 Fulham Palace Road
London W6 8JB

You might also like to visit
www.fireandwater.co.uk
The book lover's website

How to Use This Book

To make the best use of this book, you will need to know what is in it. A complete list of the words starts on the next page. It is a good idea to look up some words you know, to dip into the book and find your way around it.

This book is more than a dictionary of Maths words. It not only gives the spellings and meanings of words, but it also gives examples of how they are used in Maths and useful hints and reminders.

If you look up a word, it will never say 'see so-and-so'. It will always tell you what the word means and often where to look if you need more information. For example, if you look up **acute angle**, you will be given a quick reminder of what it is. If you need more details, you are told to look up **angles**. The entry on angles will give you full details of all the angles you might need to know about.

Under **calculators** hints are given on choosing and using a calculator. In the entries on **compasses** and **protractors**, there are reminders of how to use them. It is surprising how many children forget how to use the scales on protractors. Under **addition** you will find a list of words and phrases which mean that you need to add. There are useful sections on **fractions**, **decimals**, **graphs**, **time**, **sets** and **bases**.

This book will not teach you how to do Maths, but it should help you to understand words you are not sure of and to remember things you have forgotten.

Contents

AD

AD stands for *Anno Domini* – this means 'in the year of the Lord'. Any year from the birth of Christ onwards is AD. Years before the birth of Christ are labelled BC (before Christ).

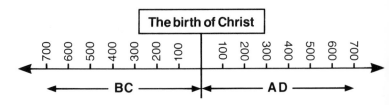

a.m.

Stands for *ante meridiem* – Latin words meaning before midday. 5 a.m. means 5 o'clock in the morning. 5 p.m. (*post meridiem*) means 5 o'clock in the afternoon. If you want to know more, look up **time**.

abacus

(The plural of abacus can be abacuses or abaci). An abacus is a counting frame. It has wires or rods fixed across it and beads which can slide to and fro along them.

A **spike abacus** has spikes or rods fixed into a base. Discs or beads can be put on or taken off each spike.

Some abaci have rails curved over like arches. You can bring forward the number of beads or discs you need and slide all the others over the top out of the way.

With a three spike or arched abacus the left can stand for hundreds, the middle for tens and the right for ones (units).

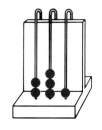

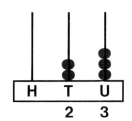

would represent two tens and three units 23.

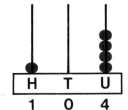

would represent one hundred, no tens and four units 104.

An abacus can have any number of spikes and may be used for counting larger numbers, for **decimals** or for counting in different **bases**. It may also be used for adding and subtracting.

acute angle

An acute angle is an angle which is less than 90°. If you want to know more, look up **angles**.

addition

Addition is counting up. We often call it adding up. You need to add up for all of these examples. The sign we use to mean 'add' is +.

Count up 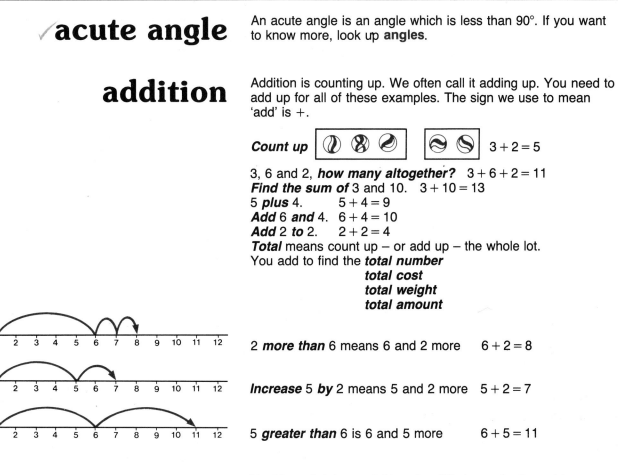 $3 + 2 = 5$

3, 6 and 2, *how many altogether?* $3 + 6 + 2 = 11$
Find the sum of 3 and 10. $3 + 10 = 13$
5 *plus* 4. $5 + 4 = 9$
Add 6 *and* 4. $6 + 4 = 10$
Add 2 *to* 2. $2 + 2 = 4$
Total means count up – or add up – the whole lot.
You add to find the ***total number***
                      total cost
                      total weight
                      total amount

2 *more than* 6 means 6 and 2 more $6 + 2 = 8$

Increase 5 *by* 2 means 5 and 2 more $5 + 2 = 7$

5 *greater than* 6 is 6 and 5 more $6 + 5 = 11$

adjacent

Next to, adjoining, neighbouring. We hear of adjacent houses, adjacent property, adjacent angles, adjacent sides of a shape.

altitude

Height.

angle of elevation

This is used when we are working out the height of something that is too tall to measure with a measuring tape.

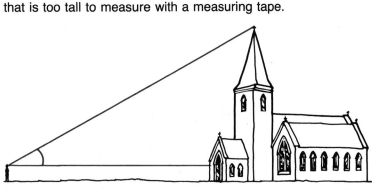

1 Look straight ahead.

2 Look at the top of the tower or whatever you are measuring. The angle of elevation is measured upwards from your first eyeline to the second.

angles

Angles are formed when two straight lines meet each other. To measure an angle we measure the amount of turn from the position of one line to the other.

Think of an opening door.
At first it is open a tiny amount and the angle is very small. The wider it opens, the larger the angle becomes.

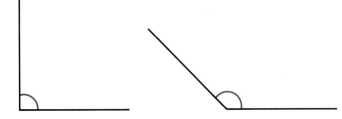

The hands of a clock turn through angles as they go round. The minute hand goes in a complete circle in one hour. A complete turn like that is measured as 360 degrees, written 360° for short.

Half a turn is 180°: this is sometimes called a **straight angle**.

A quarter of a turn is 90°.
Angles are measured using a **protractor**.

Right angles

Angles measuring 90° are called right angles. The angles at the corners of a square are all right angles. Often right angles are marked on diagrams by a small square, as in the diagrams on the left.

Acute angles

Angles that are less than 90° are called acute angles. If you have an acute pain it is sharp. Acute angles are not the wide open ones, they are less than the corner of a square.
They are also more pointed looking and 'sharper' than other kinds of angle.

Obtuse angles

Angles that are more than 90° and less than 180° are called obtuse angles.

These are wide open angles.

Reflex angles

Angles that are larger than 180° are called reflex angles.

Reflex angles are so wide open that they look as if they have been bent backwards!

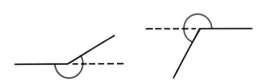

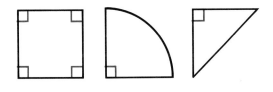

anti-clockwise

Going round in the
opposite direction
to the hands of a clock.

clockwise

anti-clockwise

apex

The highest point of something; the top.

approximately

Nearly; round about. In some books ≈ is used for
'approximately equal to'. Others use ≃.

approximations

Answers which are 'near enough'. Sometimes we do not need
an exact answer. If a rough idea is good enough then we can
use easy numbers. If we wanted to know roughly what 12
tickets would cost at 98p each we could say: 98p is nearly £1,
so 12 × 98p is nearly 12 × £1.
Our answer would be approximately £12.

We may read in a newspaper that 15000 people were at a
special event. Nobody really believes that exactly 15000 people
were there. There might have been a few more. There might
have been a few less. It doesn't matter to us. The reporter used
'round numbers' to give us an idea of the size of the crowd.
That is an approximation too.

Approximations are sometimes needed to the nearest ten, to
the nearest hundred, the nearest thousand, or even the nearest
million.

To the nearest ten
138 is nearer to 140 than to 130. It is approximately 140.

To the nearest hundred
260 is nearer to 300 than to 200. It is approximately 300.

To the nearest thousand
12040 is nearer to 12000 than 13000. It is approximately
12000.

To the nearest million
1400000 is nearer to 1000000 than to 2000000. It is
approximately 1000000.

135 is halfway between 130 and 140. We would round this up
to 140 if we needed the nearest ten. If you want to know more,
look up **rounding off**.

arc

Any part of the **circumference** of a circle is called an arc.

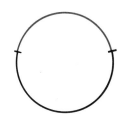

These are all arcs.

area

The **perimeter** is the distance all the way round a flat shape – the edge or the boundary. The **area** is the amount of surface space inside the perimeter. It is measured in squares. Of course all the squares must be the same size.

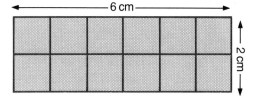

The area of the rectangle on the left would be 12 square centimetres. We can write this as $12\,cm^2$ to save time.
The quick way to find the area of a rectangle is to multiply the length by the breadth (width). But remember the answer must be a **square** measure.

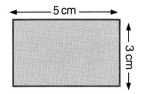

Area $= 5\,cm \times 3\,cm$
$= 15\,cm^2$

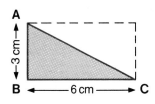

The area of a triangle is half the base $\times$ the height.
($\frac{1}{2}b \times h$ or $\frac{b \times h}{2}$ if you like.)

The area of triangle ABC is

$\frac{1}{2}$ of $6 \times 3\,cm^2$

$= \frac{1}{2}$ of $18\,cm^2$

$= 9\,cm^2$

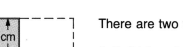

Remember that the height of a triangle is not necessarily the length of a side. Look at the one on the left here:

The dotted line is the height.

The area of this triangle is half of $7\,m \times 2\,m$.
$\frac{1}{2}$ of $14\,m^2 = 7\,m^2$

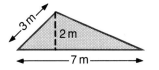

There are two ways of finding the area of a shape like this:

1 Build it up to a rectangle shape – see the dotted line. Find the area of the whole rectangle. Next find the area of the shaded rectangle: you don't want that bit! Take the unwanted bit away from the area of the large rectangle and you are left with the area of the bit you **do** want.

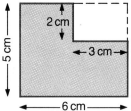

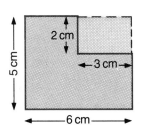

Area of large rectangle $= 5\,cm \times 6\,cm = 30\,cm^2$

Area of small shaded rectangle $= 2\,cm \times 3\,cm = 6\,cm^2$

Area of the shape we need $= 30\,cm^2 - 6\,cm^2 = 24\,cm^2$

2 The other way of finding the area of this shape is to split it up into two bits that you know how to deal with.

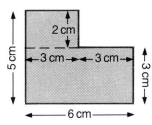

The top rectangle measures $2\,\text{cm} \times 3\,\text{cm} = 6\,\text{cm}^2$

The bottom rectangle measures $6\,\text{cm} \times 3\,\text{cm} = 18\,\text{cm}^2$

The area of the whole thing $= 18\,\text{cm}^2 + 6\,\text{cm}^2 = 24\,\text{cm}^2$

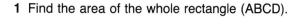

Finding the area of **borders** sometimes puzzles people, but you tackle it in just the same way.

1 Find the area of the whole rectangle (ABCD).

2 Find the area of the middle bit.

3 Take the area of the middle bit away from the area of the whole thing. Imagine the middle bit has a handle on it so that you can lift it out. Then you are left with the area of the border.

The other way of tackling it is – as with the other awkward shape – to break it up into bits you can manage.

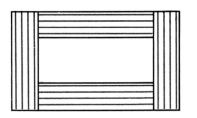

Like this

or this

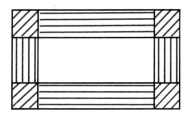

or this

You can't always choose which way you do it – it depends on which measurements you are given. Be a detective and use your clues!

asymmetrical

Not symmetrical. The two halves do not match.

asymmetry

With no symmetry. Flowers are sometimes arranged very carefully in a vase so that they are symmetrical.

symmetrical   asymmetrical

Sometimes they are arranged asymmetrically to give a different effect.

average

We talk about average height, average weight, average age, average wages, batting average and so on. In any range the average is the middle amount. To be average is to be like most other people.

If ten batsmen each scored ten runs, the average score would be ten: no one got more and no one got less. It would be very unusual though!

What if eight scored 10 each, one scored 0 and one scored 20? The way to find out the average is to add all the scores together to find the total score:

$10 + 10 + 10 + 10 + 10 + 10 + 10 + 10 + 0 + 20 = 100$

We divide the total by the number of batsmen (in this case ten):
$100 \div 10 = 10$
The average is still 10. One batsman got more, one got less, but ten was the average number. The batsman scoring 0 was below average. The batsman scoring 20 was above average.

To find the average of anything you must have a list of results:

1 Find the total (add up all the results).

2 Divide the total by the number of items – or people – in your list. The answer is the average.

In a test Paul got 22 marks, Tracy got 26, Alison got 29 and David got 31.

$$\begin{array}{r} 22 \\ 26 \\ 29 \\ \underline{31} \\ \overline{108} \end{array} = \text{total marks}$$

$$\begin{array}{r} 27 \\ 4\overline{)108} \end{array}$$

27 = average mark

This kind of average is sometimes called the ***mean*** – the mean height of a group of children is the average height.

axis, axes

Imagine someone pushes a knitting needle right through an orange from top to bottom, and then spins the orange round the needle.

That knitting needle is the **axis**. (The plural of axis is axes – say *akseez*).

An axis is a straight line through the middle of something. It can be a real line or an imaginary line. Things are arranged around it or turn around it. We say the earth turns on its axis.
Every graph has two axes.

This is the **vertical axis**

This is the **horizontal axis**

An **axis of symmetry** is a line or fold which divides a shape into two matching halves.

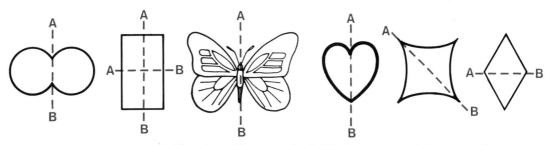

The dotted lines marked AB show some of the axes of symmetry.

BC

Stands for before Christ. 4 BC means four years before the birth of Christ. 20 BC means twenty years before the birth of Christ, so 20 BC is longer ago than 4 BC.

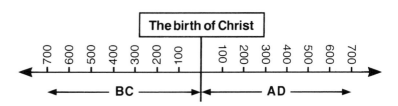

| The birth of Christ |

700 600 500 400 300 200 100 | 100 200 300 400 500 600 700

◄——— BC ———► ◄——— AD ———►

(AD stands for in the year of the Lord)

bar charts

A bar chart is a kind of **graph** where the information is shown in rows or bars. Here is one which shows the favourite colours of children in a club.

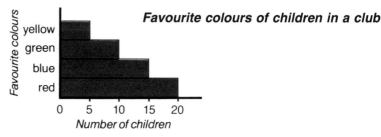

Favourite colours of children in a club

Sometimes it is easier to draw your chart the other way up.

When they are drawn this way up they are sometimes called **column graphs** or **block graphs**. The important things to remember when you are drawing any kind of graph are:

1 to give your graph a heading or title so people know what it is all about,

Favourite colours in one class

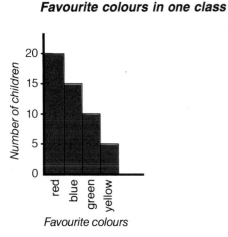

2 to label the axes so people can understand your information,

3 to fit it on to your page so that it is as easy to see and understand as possible.

Watch out for bar graphs in newspapers and advertisements.

bases

A base is a foundation – something you can build on or use as a starting point. You use a base when you make a model. A cake tin can have a loose base or a fixed one.

When we talk about the **base of a triangle**, the **base of a cube** and so on, the base is the bottom.

When we talk about **number bases** or **counting bases** we are talking about a whole pattern of counting, and the number which is at the bottom of it!

Counting in different bases: Base ten

Base ten is sometimes called the **denary** system or the **decimal** system. It is the one we normally use – probably because we have ten fingers.
When we want to count a number which is more than ten we run out of fingers.

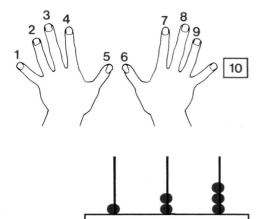

We can count 1,2,3,4,5,6,7,8,9 – then when we count the last finger we write 10. Once round! We carry on counting 1 ten and 1 (11), 1 ten and 2 (12), 1 ten and 3 (13) until we have gone all the way round twice. This is 2 tens and we write it as 20. When we have counted 10 tens we write 100.

If we count on a spike abacus we label the spikes Hundreds (10 × 10) Tens (10s) and Units (1s).

This shows 123 – 1 hundred, 2 tens and 3 units.

If we write this number down we can use column headings to remind us what each figure is worth:

H T U
1 2 3

We can collect up to 9 ones in the units column, then when we have one more we make up a bundle of ten and put that bundle in the tens column. We can collect up to 9 tens in the tens column, then when we have one more we make up a packet of ten 10s and put that packet in the hundreds column. If we had ten packets of a hundred we would have to make a parcel of them to put into another column – the thousands – and so on, and on.

Sometimes it is useful to be able to work in different bases. We can add, subtract, multiply and divide in any base. The pattern of work is just the same but instead of collecting up and sorting bundles of ten, we change the size of the bundles.

In base ten we collect up and sort out bundles of tens.
In base eight we collect up and sort out bundles of eights.
In base five we collect up and sort out bundles of fives.
In base four we collect up and sort out bundles of fours.
In base three we collect up and sort out bundles of threes.

The spike *abacus* labels would look like this:

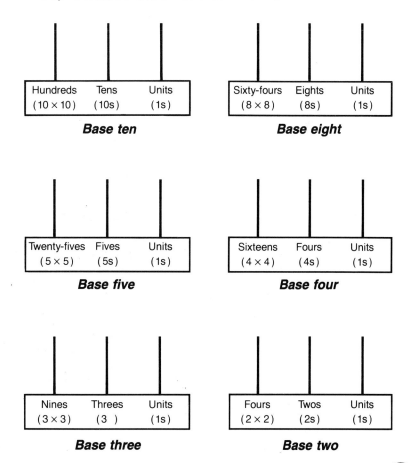

Hundreds	Tens	Units
(10 × 10)	(10s)	(1s)

Base ten

Sixty-fours	Eights	Units
(8 × 8)	(8s)	(1s)

Base eight

Twenty-fives	Fives	Units
(5 × 5)	(5s)	(1s)

Base five

Sixteens	Fours	Units
(4 × 4)	(4s)	(1s)

Base four

Nines	Threes	Units
(3 × 3)	(3)	(1s)

Base three

Fours	Twos	Units
(2 × 2)	(2s)	(1s)

Base two

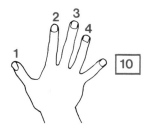

We can work with any number we like as a base. Here are some examples.

Counting in different bases: Base five

Think of counting on one hand.

We can count 1,2,3,4 – then when we count the last finger we write 10. Once round! This is not ten though, it is one group of five, so we write 10_5 or 10_{five} to show that we are using base five. We call it one-nought base five. We carry on: 1 five and 1 (11_5) 1 five and 2 (12_5), 1 five and 3 (13_5), 1 five and 4 (14_5) then we have gone all the way round twice and we write 20_5. This means two groups of five. Three groups of five is written 30_5. Four groups of five is written 40_5. When we have counted up five groups of five we write 100_5. (One nought nought, base five).

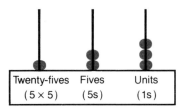

Twenty-fives (5×5)	Fives $(5s)$	Units $(1s)$

This number is 123_5

(One-two-three base five)

Its value in base ten is 1 twenty five   25
                    2 fives   10
         and 3 units   <u>3</u>
                            <u>38</u>

$123_5 = 38_{10}$ (Thirty-eight in our usual system)

Counting in different bases: Base eight

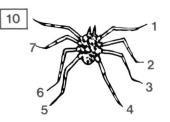

Think of a spider counting on its eight legs.

It would count 1,2,3,4,5,6,7,10. Here 10 (one-nought) means 1 group of eight, so we write 10_8. It would carry on counting 1 eight and 1 (11_8), 1 eight and 2 (12_8), 1 eight and 3 (13_8) and so on. 17_8 would mean 1 eight and 7. 20_8 would mean two groups of eight. Eight groups of eight would be 100_8.

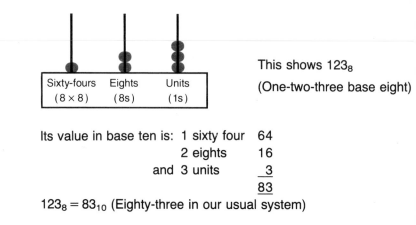

Sixty-fours (8×8)	Eights $(8s)$	Units $(1s)$

This shows 123_8

(One-two-three base eight)

Its value in base ten is: 1 sixty four   64
                      2 eights   16
        and 3 units   <u>3</u>
                           <u>83</u>

$123_8 = 83_{10}$ (Eighty-three in our usual system)

Counting in different bases: Base two

This is usually called the **binary** system. Here you can think of counting on your fists if you like – but you'll find that you run out of fists very quickly!

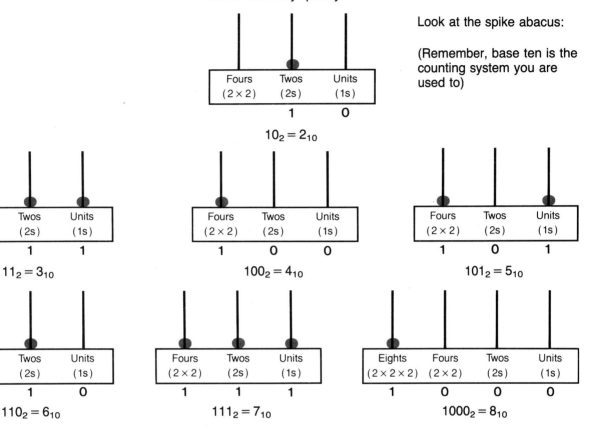

Look at the spike abacus:

(Remember, base ten is the counting system you are used to)

$10_2 = 2_{10}$

$11_2 = 3_{10}$

$100_2 = 4_{10}$

$101_2 = 5_{10}$

$110_2 = 6_{10}$

$111_2 = 7_{10}$

$1000_2 = 8_{10}$

This is how we would write base two numbers down under headings:

8s $(2 \times 2 \times 2)$	4s (2×2)	2s $(2s)$	1s $(1s)$		Base Two (Binary)		Base Ten TU
			1	=	1 one	=	1
		1	0	=	1 two	=	2
		1	1	=	1 two and 1 one	=	3
	1	0	0	=	1 four	=	4
	1	0	1	=	1 four and 1 one	=	5
	1	1	0	=	1 four and 1 two	=	6
	1	1	1	=	1 four and 1 two and 1 one	=	7
1	0	0	0	=	1 eight	=	8
1	0	0	1	=	1 eight and 1 one	=	9
1	0	1	0	=	1 eight and 1 two	=	10

The base two (binary) system is very useful because it only needs two symbols. This is the system used inside computers.

Changing numbers in different bases to base ten

We can use an abacus as we did for counting or we can put up column headings to show what all the figures are worth.
Look at these examples:
a 124_5 **b** 201_3 **c** 42_6

a Base five headings are

twenty-fives (5×5)	fives (5)	units (1)
1	2	4

124_5 is worth

1 twenty-five	25
2 fives	10
4 units	4
	39

124_5 is worth 39_{10}

b Base three headings are

nines (3×3)	threes (3)	units (1)
2	0	1

201_3 is worth –

2 nines	18
0 threes	0
1 units	1
	19

201_3 is worth 19_{10}

c Base six headings are

thirty-sixes (6×6)	sixes (6)	units (1)
	4	2

42_6 is worth

4 sixes	24
2 units	2
	26

42_6 is worth 26_{10}

Writing base ten numbers in other bases

We write down the new headings and sort the number into the new groups. Look at this example.

Write 20_{10} in base eight.
Base eight headings are needed.

$$\begin{array}{r} 2 \text{ r } 4 \\ 8\overline{)20} \end{array}$$

(8×8)	(8)	(1)
sixty-fours	eights	units
	2	4

20_{10} gives us 2 groups of eight and 4 units are left over.
$20_{10} = 24_8$
(Change 24_8 back to base ten to check the answer).

Bases greater than ten

We can work with a base of any number. We sometimes hear of the duodecimal system. This is another name for base twelve.

Base sixteen is a very useful one. It gives computer programmers a short way of writing down long binary numbers. It is sometimes called the hexadecimal system or 'hex'.

There is only one problem in working with bases greater than ten. We run out of symbols!

We have 0 1 2 3 4 5 6 7 8 9

This is fine as far as base ten. Think about base twelve though. 10_{12} (one nought base twelve) means 1 group of twelve.

We could count 1 2 3 4 5 6 7 8 9 – – 10

We need two symbols to fill in the gaps. Sometimes T and E are used. (They remind us of ten and eleven).
Sometimes A and B are used.

We could count 1 2 3 4 5 6 7 8 9 <u>A</u> <u>B</u> 10

We would carry on: 11_{12} (1 twelve and 1 unit)
12_{12} (1 twelve and 2 units)
13_{12} (1 twelve and 3 units)
19_{12} would mean 1 twelve and nine units.
$1A_{12}$ would mean 1 twelve and ten units.
$1B_{12}$ would mean 1 twelve and eleven units.
20_{12} would mean 2 groups of twelve.

For all bases greater than ten we have to use extra letters or symbols to fill in the gaps.
For base sixteen we would have six gaps.

1 2 3 4 5 6 7 8 9 (ten) (eleven) (twelve) (thirteen) (fourteen) (fifteen) 10

We could count 1 2 3 4 5 6 7 8 9 A B C D E F 10

Base sixteen

10_{16} would mean 1 group of sixteen
$1A_{16}$ would mean 1 group of sixteen and ten units
$1B_{16}$ would mean 1 group of sixteen and eleven units
$1C_{16}$ would mean 1 group of sixteen and twelve units
$1D_{16}$ would mean 1 group of sixteen and thirteen units
$1E_{16}$ would mean 1 group of sixteen and fourteen units
$1F_{16}$ would mean 1 group of sixteen and fifteen units
20_{16} would mean 2 groups of sixteen

bearings

If someone has 'lost his bearings' he is not sure which direction he is facing. Many years ago sailors used to 'take their bearings' from the Pole Star. They used to find north then they could work out the direction they should be sailing in.
When we are taking bearings we **always** start from north and

always turn clockwise to measure the angle.

1 the bearing of A from point X is 065°
2 the bearing of B from point X is 290°
It is a good idea to draw a quick diagram first when you are finding bearings or plotting a course. Draw a north direction arrow from your starting point. Whenever there is a change of course or direction draw in another north arrow and mark in the angle of the turn.

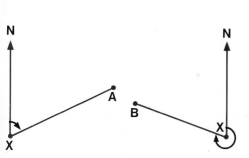

bills

There are lots of different kinds of bill but they all ask for money to be paid. It is always a good idea to check them to make sure they are asking for the right amount.
If you have been given a shopping list and a price list you can work out what the bill should come to. Don't panic, just deal with one item at a time and write everything clearly so that you can see what you are doing. Look at this example:

	£ p
2 ices at 30p each cost ($2 \times 30p$)	60
2 bags of crisps at 15p each cost ($2 \times 15p$)	30
3 drinks at 40p each cost ($3 \times 40p$)	1·20
Total cost =	£2·10

These are things which a lot of people forget:

1 A dozen is 12, half a dozen is 6. Two dozen would be 24

2 If 1 kg costs 50p
$\frac{1}{2}$kg costs ($\frac{1}{2}$ of 50p) = 25p
$1\frac{1}{2}$kg costs (50p + 25p) = 75p

3 Remember 99p is one penny less than £1.00
If some plants cost 99p each,
1 plant would cost £1.00 − 1p: 99p
2 plants would cost £2.00 − 2p: £1.98
3 plants would cost £3.00 − 3p: £2.97

You may find the entries on approximation and change useful

binary

The binary system is often called **base** 2. It is a way of counting and calculating which uses only two symbols no matter how large the number is. Everything is counted up and sorted out in groups of two instead of groups of ten.

Base 10 *our usual way of counting*	Eights ($2 \times 2 \times 2$)	Fours (2×2)	Twos (2s)	Units (1s)
1 = 1 unit				1
2 = 1 group of two			1	0
3 = 1 group of two and 1 unit			1	1
4 = 1 group of four		1	0	0
5 = 1 four and 1 unit		1	0	1
10 = 1 eight and 1 group of two	1	0	1	0

If you want to know more about this, look up **bases**.

bisect

To divide into two — usually equally. The **bi** part of the word means two as it does in **bi**cycle, **bi**plane, **bi**focal. The **sect** bit comes from the same word as section.
If we need to bisect a straight line or an angle, this can often be done by carefully folding the paper. Sometimes we need to bisect without folding and this can be done with compasses, a ruler and a pencil with a good point.

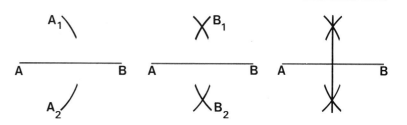

1 With the compasses open more than half the length of the line, and the point in A, draw arcs at A_1 and A_2. (Make sure your compass is done up tightly, so that it can't slip.)

2 With the compasses open the same amount and the point in B, draw arcs B_1 and B_2.

3 Join the points where the arcs cut each other.

To bisect an angle:

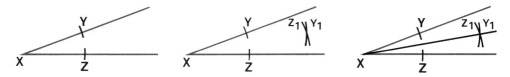

1 Put the compass point at X and draw small arcs to cut the lines each side of the angle at Y and Z.

2 Put the compass point at Y and draw an arc at Y_1, then with the compasses open the same amount still, put the point at Z and draw an arc at Z_1.

3 Join X to the point where Y_1 and Z_1 cut each other.
Hint There will be a tiny hole at the very tip of the angle at X where you first put the compass point. Prick the point where Y_1 and Z_1 cut each other. Then when you go to draw the bisecting line, you should be able to feel both pricks with your pencil point. Check that your ruler is in the best position to draw a straight line joining the two pricks.

block graphs

These are sometimes called column graphs. They are used to show information about a particular subject clearly, without using a lot of words.

Here is an example:

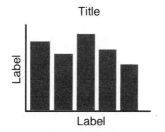

Always give your graph a title and label its axes.
If you want to know more, look up **bar charts** and **graphs**.

brackets

Brackets are used in Maths for grouping things together. They can be curved ( ) square [ ] or curly { }.

1 Brackets are put around things which need to be worked out first:
$10-3+4 = 7+4 = 11$
but $10-(3+4) = 10-7 = 3$

When you have to work out something, the order of attack is:
( )   First, work out anything in brackets
$\times \div$ Second, do any other multiplying and dividing
$+ -$ Third, do any other adding or subtracting

Look up **calculator** if you are using one for this kind of work.

2 { } Curly brackets like this are used around members of a **set**. For example:
$T = \{$ hammer, spanner, screwdriver, saw $\}$

breadth

This is width: the measurement from one side to the other.

calculate

Means 'work out'. 'Show your calculations' means show your working or show how you got the answer.

calculator

A very useful little machine. It can do a lot of working out very quickly but it can't understand problems. You have to press the right buttons to make it do the right work.

Choosing a calculator

1 See how quickly and accurately you can press the buttons on different models.

2 See if you have to hold it in one hand while you press the buttons with the other. Can you put it on a table and do the work with one hand? Is it possible to use it either way? Think how **you** will want to use it.

3 Make sure it will do all the kinds of calculation you are likely to need. It may be interesting to have a few strange signs to find out about, but there is no point in paying more money for a lot of extra buttons you are not going to use.

Using your calculator

1 Try to use the special calculator batteries. When these run out they go suddenly but they are usually accurate right to the end. Other batteries run down gradually and the calculator may give you some very odd results towards the end.

2 Some instruction leaflets are written in a very complicated way. If you have one of these don't try to sort out too much at once, and don't give up. Ask someone to help you get started and find out a bit at a time.

3 Check the calculator – and the way you are using it – sometimes. Work through some examples where you are certain you know the answers.

4 Use this plan of work: **approximate, calculate, check.**

It is very easy to make mistakes when you are pressing buttons quickly. (Just think of all the people who dial the wrong number on the telephone.) If you have a rough idea of what the result should be, you can stop yourself from giving a silly answer. Look at this example: $5{\cdot}36 \times 4$

START

↓

Approximate

↓

Calculate

↓

Check

Approximate $5 \times 4 = 20$
$5{\cdot}36 \times 4$ will be a bit more than 20

Calculate Answers of $2{\cdot}144$ or $214{\cdot}4$ could not possibly be right. $21{\cdot}44$ sounds much more likely.

Check You could use the calculator to check your answer by working out $4 \times 5{\cdot}36$ or $21{\cdot}44 \div 4$

5 There is one thing that you must be careful about. If you need to work out something like $3 + (2 \times 10)$, remember that anything in **brackets** has to be worked out first.

Some calculators have brackets signs and will do all the calculating in the right order when you press the = button. That's fine. So $3 + (2 \times 10) = 3 + 20 = 23$.

Some calculators don't have a brackets sign. Some work out each piece of the sum in the order you put it in. They would calculate $3 + 2 \times 10 = 5 \times 10 = 50$.
If your calculator does this you will have to give it the right piece of work to do first. You would have to press the piece in brackets first. 2×10 then $+ 3$. Then you would get 23.

calendar

A collection of tables showing the days and months of the year.
24 hours = 1 day
  7 days = 1 week

There is one week from one Sunday to the next Sunday. There is one week from one Monday to the next Monday. It is easy to count up the weeks by looking down the columns of a calendar.

14 days together are called a fortnight.
52 weeks = 1 year
12 months = 1 year

There is one year (12 months) from one January to the next. There is one year from one February to the next, and from one birthday to the next.
This rhyme helps us to remember how many days there are in each month:

30 days hath September,
April, June and November.
All the rest have 31,
Except February alone,
And this has 28 days clear,
But 29 in each leap year.

We always count:
365 days in 1 year
366 days in 1 *leap* year

The calendar we use is called the Gregorian calendar after Pope Gregory. His experts helped to sort it out. Normally a leap year comes once every four years: 1984, 1988, 1992 and so on. If you want to know more, look up **leap year**.

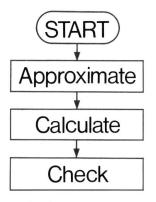

JUNE

Sun	Mon	Tue	Wed	Thu	Fri	Sat
			1	2	3	4
5	6	7	8	9	10	11
12	13	14	15	16	17	18
19	20	21	22	23	24	25
26	27	28	29	30		

cancelling

In Maths we use cancelling when we divide the **numerator** and the **denominator** of a fraction by the same number. This does not change the value of the fraction but it gives us smaller numbers to work with.

$$\frac{4}{16} = \frac{4 \times 1}{4 \times 4} = \frac{1}{4} \qquad \frac{2}{8} = \frac{2 \times 1}{2 \times 4} = \frac{1}{4} \qquad \frac{9}{12} = \frac{3 \times 3}{3 \times 4} = \frac{3}{4}$$

These are examples of cancelling.

Here are some more:

$$\frac{\cancel{3}^{1}}{\cancel{6}_{2}} = \frac{1}{2} \qquad \frac{\cancel{6}^{2}}{\cancel{9}_{3}} = \frac{2}{3} \qquad \frac{\cancel{10}^{2}}{\cancel{15}_{3}} = \frac{2}{3}$$

We often cancel when we reduce a fraction to its lowest terms, and when we multiply or divide fractions.

Remember The numerator and the denominator **must** be divided by the same number.
If you have forgotten about this, look up **fractions**.

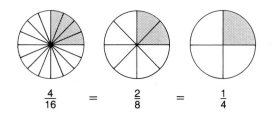

$$\frac{4}{16} \quad = \quad \frac{2}{8} \quad = \quad \frac{1}{4}$$

capacity

Capacity is the amount that something will hold.
We talk about:
– the capacity of a car boot
– the capacity of a Thermos flask
– the capacity of a freezer, of a watering can,
  of a petrol tank and so on.

Capacity can be measured in different ways. The amount of liquid something will hold is measured in old style pints and gallons or in metric measures of litres.

8 pints   = 1 gallon
1000 millilitres = 1 litre

1 gallon is about $4\frac{1}{2}$ litres. 1 litre is about $1\frac{3}{4}$ pints. The plastic teaspoon the chemist gives with a bottle of medicine holds 5 ml (millilitres).

Sometimes cubic centimetres are used for measuring small quantities. Some older books show cubic centimetres as c.c. for short. cm^3 is used now (1000 cm^3 = 1 litre.)

Cubic feet or cubic metres are sometimes used for measuring larger amounts like the capacity of a car boot or of a freezer.

Celsius centigrade

Celsius was a Swedish scientist and the modern Celsius temperature scale is named after him. °C stands for degrees centigrade, or for degrees Celsius. The scale is the same.
   0 °C is the freezing point of water
100 °C is the boiling point of water.

These are both marked on the thermometer and the space in between is divided into one hundred degrees. The normal temperature of human blood is 36·9 °C. A minus sign (−) before a number of degrees means that the temperature is below freezing point. −5 °C (minus 5 degrees Celsius) means 5° below freezing point.

centimetre

A centimetre is a measurement of length. This line ——— is one centimetre long (1 cm). Any word with *centi* in it has something to do with 100.

1 cm is $\frac{1}{100}$ of a metre

100 cm = 1 metre

$2\frac{1}{2}$ cm is about 1 inch in the old measurements.

30 cm is about 1 foot.

century

A century is 100 years. 1910 and 1990 are in the 20th century. 1842 is in the 19th century. This is not as silly as it sounds. The first hundred years AD 1 to 100 are the *first* century, so 100 to 199 are the *second* century. 200 to 299 are the *third* century and so on. See also AD and BC.

change

When we get change so that we can use a slot machine, we still have the same amount of money. It's just made up differently. We might get 5 ten pence pieces for a fifty pence piece.

Buying and selling is not quite the same. If we don't have exactly the right money to pay the shopkeeper for what we want, we give him a bit too much and he gives us the *change*. The change is the difference between the price of what we are buying and the money we give the shopkeeper.

We give the shopkeeper   50p

The sweets we wanted cost   40p

The change was   10p

50p − 40p = 10p

You can always find the difference between two amounts by taking the smaller amount away from the larger.

Another way is 'counting on'.

40p + (10p) = 50p. The change is 10p.

Shopkeepers often count on from the price as they put your change into your hand.

Shop price ↓ 　　　　　　　　　　　　　　　　　　*I paid* ↓

7p　　　　　+ 2 p　　　　　+ 1p　　　=　　　10p

Change = 3p.

chord

A chord is a straight line which joins two points on the **circumference** of a circle.

AB and CD are both chords.

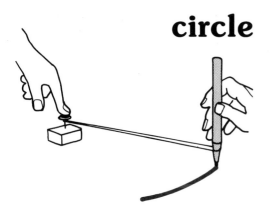

circle

If you are very careful you can draw a circle with a loop of thread, a drawing pin and a pencil. The drawing pin marks the centre of the circle – make sure it doesn't stick into the table! Press it into something which doesn't matter.

Hold the drawing pin still with one finger. Keep the thread tight and mark the paper all the way round with the pencil.
It is easier to use compasses to draw circles. Look up **compasses** if you are not sure how to use them.
A complete turn in a circle is measured as 360 degrees (360°).

Here is a list of useful words to do with circles which you can look up: **circumference, radius, diameter, semi-circle, quadrant, arc, chord, segment, sector, tangent**.

circumference

The circumference is the distance all the way round a circle. It is the boundary line.

The circumference of a circle is always just over three times the length of its diameter. We use the Greek letter π (pi) to stand for this amount. It is about 3·142 or $3\frac{1}{7}$.
The diameter $(d) \times \pi =$ the circumference of the circle.
The radius $(r) \times 2 \times \pi =$ the circumference of the circle.
To save time we say:

> The circumference of a circle $= \pi d$ or $2\pi r$

The area of a circle is $\pi \times r \times r$

To save time we say:

> The area of a circle $= \pi r^2$

If you want to know more, look up **circles**.

circumscribe

To draw a shape round the outside of another shape so that it *just* touches it.

This triangle circumscribes the circle.

This circle circumscribes the triangle.

Scribe comes from the Latin word for 'write'.
Circum is Latin for 'around'.
(Think about *circum*ference too.)

clinometer

Any word ending in metre or meter has something to do with measuring. A **clino**meter is used to measure an in**cline** – a slope. It can be used to measure the angle of elevation when we are working out the height of something.

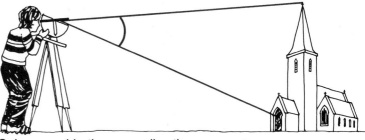

clockwise

Going round in the same direction as the hands of a clock.

collinear

This means in the same straight line. Points which are collinear are in the same straight line if they are joined together.

common denominator

The denominator is the bottom number of a fraction. It is the name of the fraction and tells us what sort it is. We can only add fractions together (or take them away) if they have the same denominator.

2 fifths + 1 fifth = 3 fifths

$$\frac{2}{5} \quad + \quad \frac{1}{5} \quad = \quad \frac{3}{5}$$

4 fifths − 3 fifths = 1 fifth

$$\frac{4}{5} \quad - \quad \frac{3}{5} \quad = \quad \frac{1}{5}$$

If we are dealing with different **kinds** of fractions we have to change them to the same kind before we can add or subtract them. We have to find a denominator which will fit them both. It is common to them both and is called a **common denominator**.

Look at $\frac{1}{2} + \frac{1}{4}$

We can change $\frac{1}{2}$ into quarters $\frac{1}{2} = \frac{2}{4}$

$$\frac{1}{2} + \frac{1}{4}$$

$$= \frac{2}{4} + \frac{1}{4}$$

The common denominator is 4.
Each denominator will divide exactly into the common denominator.
4 will divide into 4 exactly.
2 will divide into 4 exactly.

For $\frac{1}{3} + \frac{2}{9}$ 9 could be the common denominator
    3 will divide into 9 exactly
    9 will divide into 9 exactly
    Both fractions could be changed to ninths.

For $\frac{1}{2} + \frac{1}{3}$ 6 could be the common denominator
    2 will divide into 6 exactly
    3 will divide into 6 exactly
    Both fractions could be changed to sixths.

If you want to know more, look up **fractions**.

commutative

Something which is commutative can be changed from place to place. You may have heard of the **commutative law** or the **commutative property**. This just means that when we are adding up or multiplying we can change the numbers from place to place and deal with them in any order we like. The answer will be the same.

$3 + 5 = 8$
$5 + 3 = 8$

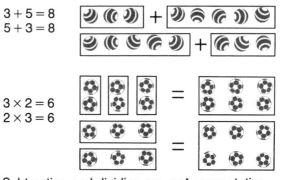

$3 \times 2 = 6$
$2 \times 3 = 6$

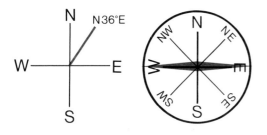

Subtracting and dividing are **not** commutative.
$10 - 3$ is not the same as $3 - 10$
$10 \div 2$ is not the same as $2 \div 10$.

compass

A compass is used for finding direction. The magnetised needle in the middle can swing to and fro freely and it always points north. If you move the compass round until the needle is exactly over the direction marked N or north you can find all the other directions. The ones we use mostly are north, south, east and west (N, S, E and W). In between come north-west, north-east, south-east and south-west (NW, NE, SE, SW). These are called points of the compass.
There are 32 points of the compass altogether.

Some compasses have degrees marked on them. A complete circle is 360 degrees (360°).
N 36° E means from the north measure 36° towards the east.
S 68° W means from the south measure 68° towards the west.

compasses

(We talk about a pair of compasses like a pair of scissors.)

Compasses are used for drawing circles and parts of circles (arcs). Before you start to use compasses make sure you have a good point on your pencil.

1 Screw the pencil in firmly, making sure that the compass point and the pencil point are level.

2 Open the legs of the compasses.

3 Put the compass point where you want the middle of your circle to be. Make sure the point doesn't go into the table.

4 Hold the compasses at the top so you don't squeeze the legs together.

5 Keep the compass point in its hole and swing the pencil leg first in one direction then in the other so that the pencil point can mark out the circle.

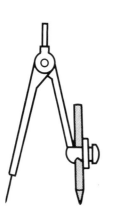

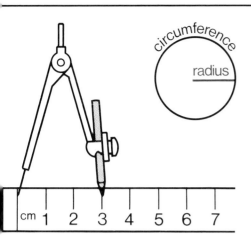

Practise until you are making good circles then you can experiment with the compasses and try making patterns. The compass point always goes at the centre of the circle and the pencil point always marks out the **circumference**.

The distance between the centre of the circle and the circumference is called the **radius**.
If you have to draw a circle with a radius of – say – 3 cm, make sure that the compass point and the pencil point are exactly 3 cm apart before you start drawing your circle.

Use a ruler to measure the gap.

'Set your compasses at 30 mm' means open the compasses so that the pencil point and the compass point are exactly 30 mm apart.

complementary angles

If two angles added together make 90° they are called complementary angles.

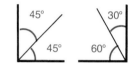

concentric

With the same centre.
These circles are concentric.

cone

A cone is a solid shape with a flat circular base. Its top is pointed. Its sides are curved.
The top is sometimes called the *apex*.

congruent

Congruent means exactly the same size and shape. Two circles are congruent if they have the same radius. They would fit exactly on top of each other.

These triangles are congruent.

constant

If people grumble about a constant noise they mean a noise which goes on all the time and never stops.
In Maths something is called a constant if it has the same value all the time and never changes.
Sometimes a letter is used to stand for an amount in an equation. If it just stands for one amount which stays the same, it is called a constant.
If it can stand for any one of a whole range of amounts it is called a *variable*.
A constant stays constantly the same.
A variable can change.

constructions

In Maths, constructions are drawings which are built up carefully and accurately. Usually a pair of compasses, a ruler and a sharp pencil are needed. Sometimes a set square or a protractor are useful. The drawing of a triangle to exact measurements is one example of a construction. To construct a triangle with sides of 5 cm, 4 cm and 3 cm:

1

A ———————— B
5 cm

1 Draw a line exactly 5 cm long. If you want it to be the base line leave space above it for the rest of the triangle.

2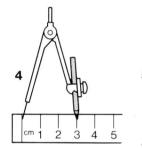

3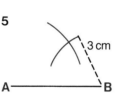
4 cm
A ———————— B

2 Open your compasses so that the compass point and pencil point are exactly 4 cm apart.

3 With the compass point at A and the compasses open 4 cm, draw an arc. Any point on this arc must be 4 cm away from A.

4

5
3 cm
A ———————— B

4 Open the compasses 3 cm exactly.

5 With the compass point at B draw an arc to cut the arc you drew from A. The point where the two arcs cut each other must be 4 cm from A and 3 cm from B.
Call this point C.

6
C
A ———————— B

6 Join AC and BC.

Look up **bisect** if you want to know about constructions to bisect a line or an angle.

conversion

A conversion is a change from one thing to another. If we make a conversion we convert something into something else. Read **convert**. It comes next.

convert

To convert means to change.
If you are going to France you will have to convert your own money into francs. You will be given different money but it will have the same value as your own money.

If you have a ruler marked in inches and you need to measure something in centimetres you will have to convert the inches into centimetres. You will have different numbers, but they will measure the same length.

Changing units

If you break something up into smaller pieces, you will have more pieces than when you started. If you change a unit to something smaller you will have more of the smaller units. If you change £1 to pennies you will have 100p. If you change £2 to pennies you will have 200p (2 × 100p). More, so you multiply.

If you change your unit to something bigger you will have less of them. If you change 100 pennies into pounds you will only have £1. You divide the number of pennies by 100.

To change p to £ divide   by 100
£ to p multiply by 100

To change mm to cm divide   by   10
cm to m divide   by   100
m to km divide   by 1000
cm to mm multiply by   10
m to cm multiply   by   100
km to m multiply   by 1000

To change g to kg divide   by 1000
kg to g multiply by 1000

ml to l divide   by 1000
l to ml multiply by 1000

Changing from the metric system into units in the Imperial system is not so easy. Here is a table to help you.

To convert	into	multiply by
metres	inches	39·37
litres	pints	1·76
kilograms	pounds	2·20
kilometres	miles	0·63
hectares	acres	2·47
inches	centimetres	2·54
pints	litres	0·57
ounces	grams	28·35
pounds	grams	453·59
acres	hectares	0·40
miles	kilometres	1·61

To convert °C to °F

°C (degrees centigrade or Celsius) to °F (degrees Fahrenheit): Multiply the number of °C by $\frac{9}{5}$ then add 32°.

To convert °F to °C

Take 32° from the number of °F then multiply the answer by $\frac{5}{9}$.

Sometimes it can be useful to draw a ***conversion graph*** with one set of values on the vertical axis and the other along the horizontal axis. When you have plotted enough points you can read off a number of conversions very quickly.

co-ordinates

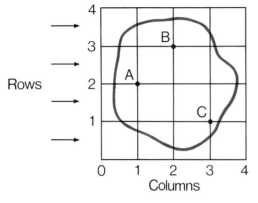

Rows

Columns

Co-ordinates are two numbers or letters which help us to find the exact position of something. They are often used on maps, graphs and charts.
Here is an example. Look at the diagram on the left.

The numbers start from 0 in the bottom left corner

The point A is 1 square along and 2 squares up.
We write this as (1, 2).
The co-ordinates of A are (1, 2).
The point at B is 2 squares along and 3 squares up.
We write this as (2, 3).
The co-ordinates of B are (2, 3).
To find a point we look **along** and then **up**.
(Some people remember this by saying, 'Along the hall then up the stairs!')
The co-ordinates (3, 1) lead us to the point at C.

cross-section

1　　　**2**　　　**3**

When we look at a cross-section of something we can see what it is like inside,
for example:
1 A cross-section of a cucumber
2 A cross-section of some seaside rock
3 A cross-section of an apple.

A cross-section is made by cutting straight across something.

cube

A square box shape.

A cube has six faces. (Four sides, a top and a bottom.)
Every face of a cube is a square. All of these squares are the same size.
A cube has eight **vertices** (corners).

To find the volume of a cube we multiply the length × breadth × height.
(Make sure all the measurements are in the same units – all centimetres or all metres, for example.)
A cube which has a side of 3 cm will have a volume of
$3 \times 3 \times 3$ **cubic** centimetres
　$= 9 \times 3$ cubic centimetres
　$= 27$ 　cubic centimetres
This can be written 27 cm^3 to save time.

cubed numbers

1 cubed means $1 \times 1 \times 1$
It is written as 1^3
$1^3 = 1$

2 cubed means $2 \times 2 \times 2$
It is written as 2^3
$2^3 = 8$

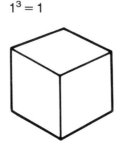

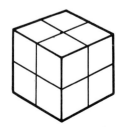

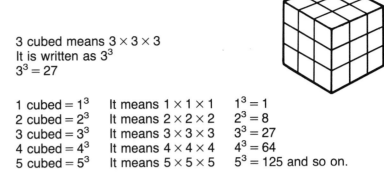

3 cubed means $3 \times 3 \times 3$
It is written as 3^3
$3^3 = 27$

1 cubed = 1^3	It means $1 \times 1 \times 1$	$1^3 = 1$
2 cubed = 2^3	It means $2 \times 2 \times 2$	$2^3 = 8$
3 cubed = 3^3	It means $3 \times 3 \times 3$	$3^3 = 27$
4 cubed = 4^3	It means $4 \times 4 \times 4$	$4^3 = 64$
5 cubed = 5^3	It means $5 \times 5 \times 5$	$5^3 = 125$ and so on.

cuboid

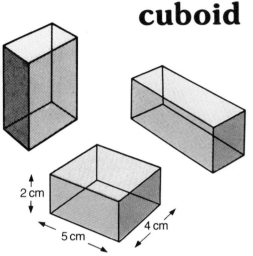

A cuboid is a rectangular box shape.
It has six faces (4 sides, a top and a bottom).
All the faces are rectangles.
The top matches the bottom, the ends match each other and the opposite sides match each other.
A cuboid has eight **vertices** (corners).

To find the volume of a cuboid we multiply the length $\times$ breadth $\times$ height.
(Remember, the measurements must all be in the same units – all centimetres or all metres for example.)
The answer will be a **cubic** measure.
The volume of a cuboid measuring 5 cm long by 4 cm wide by 2 cm high would be:

$5 \times 4 \times 2$ cubic centimetres
$= 20 \times 2$ cubic centimetres
$= 40$ cubic centimetres

This can be written 40 cm³ to save time.

cylinder

A cylinder is a roller shape. Its ends are flat circles. These circles are parallel to each other. A cylinder has the same diameter all through. It doesn't get thicker or thinner.

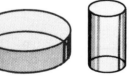

dates

Dates are often written in numbers.

25th December 1986 can be written as 25.12.86, the 25th day of the 12th month in 1986.
5.11.85 means the 5th day of the 11th month in 1985, the 5th November 1985.

In this country we always put the number of the day first, then the number of the month, then the year. Some digital watches show the days and months the other way round. If you have one of these you must be careful not to confuse everybody. Always write the day first!
It is always useful to know your own date of birth in numbers, so that you can fill in forms.

Ages

If someone's date of birth is before yours, he is older than you. He was born before you. He has been alive longer than you. Someone born in 1980 is older than someone born in 1981. Someone born in July 1981 is older than someone born in August 1981.

Counting from one date to another

If you count from one date to another, don't count the first date unless you are told that the dates are *inclusive*.
From 1st June to 2nd June is one whole day. From 2nd May to 20th May there are 18 days. You can count on from 2 to 20

$2 + \boxed{18} = 20$

Or you can find the difference between the two dates

$20 - 2 = \boxed{18}$

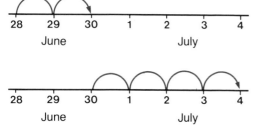

Here is an example where the days run into different months. How many days are there from 28th June to 4th July?
There are 30 days in June.
28th to 30th June = 2 days
30th June to 4th July = 4 days
Altogether 28th June to 4th July = 6 days
You can use a calendar to help you if you have one.

Sometimes you may need to know a number of years.
Here is an example:
King Henry VIII ruled from 1509 to 1547. How many years was this?
We can work this out by counting on from 1509 to 1547.
From 1509 to 1510 is 1 year
        1510 to 1547 is 37 years
Altogether 1509 to 1547 is 38 years.
Or we can find the difference between the two dates by taking the earlier one from the later one.

$$\begin{array}{r} 1547 \\ -\ 1509 \\ \hline 38 \text{ years} \end{array}$$

Sometimes dates are written in Roman numbers. If you want to know more, look up **Roman numerals**.

decade

A decade is ten years.
Something which happened during the last decade happened during the last ten years.

decagon

A decagon is a flat shape with ten straight sides and ten angles. If all the sides and angles are equal it is called a *regular decagon*.

regular decagon

irregular decagon

decimals

We are used to counting in hundreds, tens and units. That is the decimal way of counting. Decimals are all about tens of things and tenths of things.

The decimal point separates the whole numbers from the decimal fractions. The decimal point just marks the place. Everything before it is a whole number. Everything after it is a fraction. Decimal fractions are tenths, hundredths, thousandths and so on.

Place value

		H	T	U
3 is worth 3 units				3
30 is worth 3 tens			3	0
300 is worth 3 hundreds		3	0	0

We can tell what the 3 is worth by its place.

The first figure after the decimal point shows a number of tenths. $0.3 = \frac{3}{10}$

The second figure after the decimal point shows a number of hundredths. $0.03 = \frac{3}{100}$

The third figure after the decimal point shows thousandths. $0.003 = \frac{3}{1000}$

Look what happens if we start off with 0·3 and multiply by 10.

	Th	H	T	U·	$\frac{1}{10}$(t)
				0·	3
$0.3 \times 10 =$				3	
$3 \times 10 =$			3	0	
$30 \times 10 =$		3	0	0	
$300 \times 10 =$	3	0	0	0	

Whenever we make our number ten times bigger we need an extra column to put in it. We push it one place to the left. We could go on and on adding more columns to the left but we don't often need numbers that big!

Start off with 3000 and divide it by 10.

		Th	H	T	U·	$\frac{1}{10}$(t)	$\frac{1}{100}$(h)	$\frac{1}{1000}$(th)
		3	0	0	0			
3000	$\div 10 =$		3	0	0			
300	$\div 10 =$			3	0			
30	$\div 10 =$				3			
3	$\div 10 =$				0·	3		
0·3	$\div 10 =$				0·	0	3	
0·03	$\div 10 =$				0·	0	0	3

Whenever we make our number ten times smaller we push it one place to the right. We could go on and on adding columns to the right but we rarely need fractions that small!

Remember there is a very easy way to multiply or divide decimals by 10.

To multiply decimals by 10 move your figures one place to the left.

To multiply decimals by 100 move your figures two places to the left.

To multiply decimals by 1000 move your figures three places to the left.

Write down the column headings if it helps you.

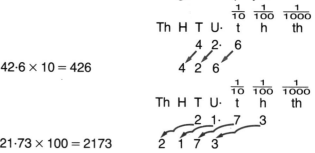

42·6 × 10 = 426

21·73 × 100 = 2173

To divide decimals by 10 we make them ten times smaller. We move the figures one place to the right.
To divide decimals by 100 we move the figures two places to the right.
To divide decimals by 1000 we move the figures three places to the right.

$$\frac{1}{10} \quad \frac{1}{100} \quad \frac{1}{1000}$$
Th H T U· t   h   th
                1· 2
            0· 1   2

1·2 ÷ 10 = 0·12

$$\frac{1}{10} \quad \frac{1}{100} \quad \frac{1}{1000}$$
Th H T U· t   h   th
                1· 2
            0· 0   1   2

1·2 ÷ 100 = 0·012

We have to put the nought in after the decimal point to show there are no tenths.

Of course you can multiply or divide in the ordinary way if you like but this way is quicker.

Noughts just mean 'we haven't got any of these.'

Here are some examples.

12·0   0·4   10·6   0·03   3·20   3·02

$$\frac{1}{10} \quad \frac{1}{100}$$
H T U· t   h

1 2 · 0   means 12 whole ones, no fractions
                12·0 = 12

   0 · 4   means we have no whole numbers but we do
                have 4 tenths
                $0.4 = \frac{4}{10}$

1 0 · 6   means 1 ten, no units, 6 tenths
                $10.6 = 10\frac{6}{10}$

   0 · 0   3   means we have no whole numbers and no
                tenths but we do have 3 hundredths
                $0.03 = \frac{3}{100}$

   3 · 2   0   means 3 units, 2 tenths and no hundredths.
                We could just write 3·2 if we liked. It would
                mean the same thing.

$$\frac{1}{10} \quad \frac{1}{100}$$

H T U · t h

$3 \cdot 0 \quad 2 \ = 3\frac{2}{100}$ Here you **must** put the nought in to show there are no tenths. This keeps the 2 in the hundredths column.

$$\frac{1}{10} = \frac{10}{100}$$

Remember one tenth is more than one hundredth.

0·8 is more than 0·15

$0.8 = \frac{8}{10}$ This would be $\frac{80}{100}$

$0.15 = \frac{1}{10}$ and $\frac{5}{100}$ This would be only $\frac{15}{100}$

Useful decimals to learn

$0.75 \ = \frac{3}{4}$ $0.2 \ = \frac{1}{5} \ (\frac{1}{5} = \frac{2}{10})$

$0.5 \ \ \ = \frac{1}{2}$ $0.1 \ = \frac{1}{10}$

$0.25 \ = \frac{1}{4}$ $0.01 = \frac{1}{100}$

$0.125 = \frac{1}{8}$

Adding and subtracting decimals

If you can add and subtract hundreds, tens and units you can add and subtract decimals. The only thing to remember is to keep the decimal points under one another. This keeps all the figures lined up in the correct columns.

```
   12·5
+   9·86
   22·36
    11
```

Multiplying and dividing decimals by a whole number

Remember to put your decimal point in the answer. Keep the decimal points underneath each other. Multiply – or divide – in your usual way.

```
   4·6          52·07          6·5
×    2       ×      5      5)32.²5
   9·2          260·35
    1            1   3
```

Multiplying by a decimal fraction

```
    46           46            4·6
×    3       ×   0·3       ×   0·3
   138          13·8          1·38
    1            1             1
```

1 Don't take any notice of the decimal points. Multiply the numbers in your usual way.

2 Count up the number of figures after decimal points in the numbers you started with.

That is the number of figures which should come after the decimal point in your answer.

$46 \times 3 = 138$
$46 \times \underline{\cdot 3} = 13 \cdot \underline{8}$ (one figure after a point)
$4 \cdot \underline{6} \times \cdot \underline{3} = 1 \cdot \underline{38}$ (two figures after points)
$0 \cdot \underline{46} \times \cdot \underline{3} = 0 \cdot \underline{138}$ (three figures after points).

Look at these examples too:

$3 \times 2 = 6$
$0 \cdot 3 \times 2 = 0 \cdot 6$
$0 \cdot 3 \times 0 \cdot 2 = 0 \cdot 06$
$0 \cdot 03 \times 0 \cdot 2 = 0 \cdot 006$

$4 \cdot 2 \times 3 \cdot 5$

$$
\begin{array}{r}
42 \\
\times \quad 35 \\
\hline
1260 \\
210 \\
\hline
1470 \\
\end{array}
$$

$4 \cdot 2 \times 3 \cdot 5$ Two figures come after points.
$42 \times 35 = 1470$
$4 \cdot 2 \times 3 \cdot 5 = 14 \cdot 70$

Dividing by a decimal fraction

Dividing by a decimal fraction is easier if we make it a whole number first. We can multiply both numbers by 10 and we do not change the answer. Look again at the boxes below.

$12 \div 2 = 6$ $120 \div 20 = 6$	$10 \div 1 = 10$ $100 \div 10 = 10$	$6 \div 3 = 2$ $60 \div 30 = 2$

$3 \cdot 5 \div 0 \cdot 7$

1 Multiply both numbers by 10. This gets rid of the decimal points.

$35 \div 7 = 5$

2 Divide in your usual way.
$3 \cdot 5 \div 0 \cdot 7 = 5$

$24 \div 1 \cdot 2$

1 Multiply both numbers by 10.

$240 \div 12 = 20$

2 Divide in the usual way.
$24 \div 1 \cdot 2 = 20$

$6 \div 0 \cdot 3 =$ $6 \div 0 \cdot 3 = 20$

$60 \div 3 = 20$

If we have two figures after a decimal point we multiply both numbers by 100 to get rid of the point.
$48 \div 0 \cdot 12 = 4800 \div 12$
$3 \cdot 4 \div 0 \cdot 02 = 340 \div 2$

decrease

To decrease is to make something less. It is the opposite of increase.
If taxes are decreased people pay less money.
Decrease your speed means lessen your speed – slow down.
Decreasing the number of stitches on a needle will make the knitting narrower.
To decrease 20 by 5 you start with 20 and take 5 away from it. You make it 5 less.

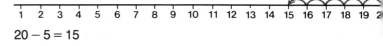

$20 - 5 = 15$

deduct

If you deduct something you take it away. If you break a window the cost of a new one may be deducted from your pocket money. A deduction is an amount which is taken away.

degrees

In Maths some measurements are made in degrees. A little circle in the air ° stands for the word degree.

There are 360 degrees (360°) in a **circle**.
Angles are measured in degrees using a protractor.
A right angle measures 90°.

Temperatures are measured in degrees on a thermometer.
°C means degrees **Celsius** (this is often called centigrade.)
°F means degrees on the **Fahrenheit** scale.

deltahedron

A deltahedron is a solid shape which has an equilateral triangle for each face. (The plural is deltahedra.)

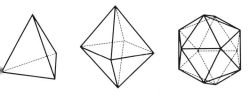

If you want to know more, look up **polyhedron** (a solid shape with many faces.)

denary

Denary means something to do with ten. The denary system is the one we are all brought up with – hundreds, tens and units and so on. Everything is sorted out in groups of ten. Sometimes it is called the **decimal** system or **base ten**.

denominator

The bottom number of a fraction is called the de**nom**inator. It is the **name** of the fraction and tells us what sort it is. Without looking at the top number (the **numerator**) we can tell:

$\frac{\blacksquare}{2}$ – something has been divided into 2 equal pieces or groups. We have a number of halves.

$\frac{\blacksquare}{3}$ – something has been divided into three equal pieces or groups. We have a number of thirds.

$\frac{\blacksquare}{5}$ – something has been divided into five equal pieces or groups. We have a number of fifths.

There is more information which might be helpful under **common denominator** and **fractions**.

diagonal

1 When it is describing something, diagonal means sloping, slanting.

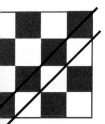

This is a diagonal row.

This is a diagonal row.

This counter has made a diagonal move. It has moved diagonally.

2 A diagonal is also the name we give to a straight line which slopes from one corner of a shape to another corner.

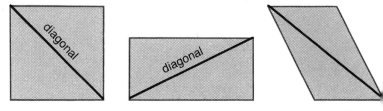

It is possible to draw five diagonals in this shape. AC, AD, BE and BD and CE.

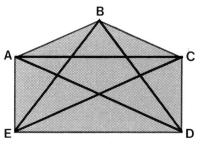

(Lines joining corners which are next to each other are **sides** of the shape. They are not called diagonals of the shape.)

diagrams

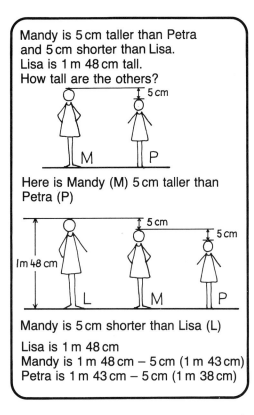

Mandy is 5 cm taller than Petra and 5 cm shorter than Lisa.
Lisa is 1 m 48 cm tall.
How tall are the others?

Here is Mandy (M) 5 cm taller than Petra (P)

Mandy is 5 cm shorter than Lisa (L)

Lisa is 1 m 48 cm
Mandy is 1 m 48 cm − 5 cm (1 m 43 cm)
Petra is 1 m 43 cm − 5 cm (1 m 38 cm)

A diagram is an outline drawing. It can be a chart or a map or a simple picture. Sometimes it can take a lot of words to give directions or to explain something. It can sound very complicated. Very often a diagram can be quicker and easier to understand. It can show information clearly without using many words at all.

Pie charts, **functions** (mapping), **nomograms**, **graphs** and **Venn diagrams** are examples of this. There is a section on each of these in this book. Diagrams are helpful when we are finding areas, volumes or bearings, when we are plotting a course, or dealing with circles, or stuck on a problem.

If you are stuck on a problem it is a good idea to draw a quick picture or diagram. Mark in all the information you are given in the question. Label everything you can. It may help you to see what else you can work out and label. It will help you to see what the problem is all about.

Diagrams in books are often numbered so that it is easy to tell you which one to look at. Sometimes they are called 'figures'. 'See figure 4' (or fig. 4).

Remember diagrams are not always drawn to scale. You must not count one line as twice the length of another one just because it looks as if it is. You must look at the labels and the information you are given.
If you are drawing a diagram to explain something to someone else remember to make it as easy to see as possible. Label everything clearly and make sure you have put in everything people need to know.

You may find it helpful to read the section on **problems**.

diameter

A diameter is a straight line drawn right through the centre of a **circle**. It divides the circle into two halves.

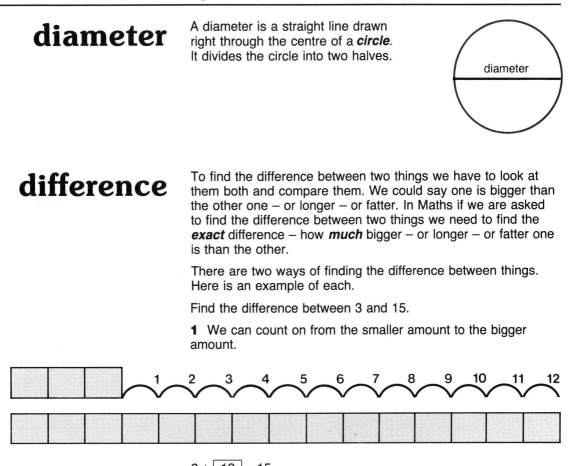

difference

To find the difference between two things we have to look at them both and compare them. We could say one is bigger than the other one – or longer – or fatter. In Maths if we are asked to find the difference between two things we need to find the **exact** difference – how **much** bigger – or longer – or fatter one is than the other.

There are two ways of finding the difference between things. Here is an example of each.

Find the difference between 3 and 15.

1 We can count on from the smaller amount to the bigger amount.

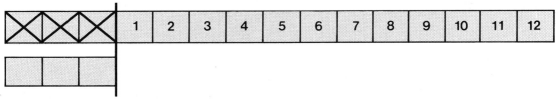

$3 + \boxed{12} = 15$

The difference between 3 and 15 is 12.

2 We can write down the larger amount and take the smaller amount away from it.

$$
\begin{array}{r}
15 \\
-3 \\
\hline
12
\end{array}
$$

The difference between 3 and 15 is 12.
The second way is probably easier if you are dealing with large numbers or awkward amounts. Do remember to write down the larger amount first or you will get in a muddle.

digits

The digits are the figures or symbols which make up a number. We normally use ten digits 0 1 2 3 4 5 6 7 8 and 9 to make up all the numbers we need.
426 has 3 digits
 91 has 2 digits
 33 is a two digit number too.

dimensions

These are measurements of size. We usually think of **length**, **width**, **height** and **radius**. It is useful to know your dimensions before you go out to buy new clothes. The dimensions of the rooms are usually marked on the plans of a house.

directed numbers

Directed numbers can be positive (+) or negative (−).

A temperature of −5°C means the temperature is 5°C below zero (freezing point). A temperature of +5°C means the temperature is 5°C above zero (freezing point).

A number with a minus sign before it is called a negative number. A number with a plus sign before it is called a positive number. If there is no sign before a number it is always counted as positive. If we are just told that a temperature is 10°C we always count that as 10°C above freezing point.

If we draw a number line vertically the positive numbers are always put above the zero — going up. The negative numbers are below zero — going down. Think of a lift.

3	three floors up
2	two floors up
1	one floor up
0	ground floor

− 1	one floor down
− 2	two floors down
− 3	three floors down

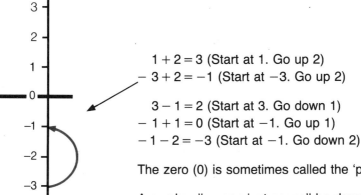

1 + 2 = 3 (Start at 1. Go up 2)
− 3 + 2 = −1 (Start at −3. Go up 2)

3 − 1 = 2 (Start at 3. Go down 1)
− 1 + 1 = 0 (Start at −1. Go up 1)
− 1 − 2 = −3 (Start at −1. Go down 2)

The zero (0) is sometimes called the 'point of origin'.

A number line can just as well be drawn horizontally:

−2 + 1 = −1
−2 + 2 = 0

−2 − 2 = −4
+1 − 2 = −1

discount

Discount often means a 'special offer'. Discount is an amount of money which can be taken off the cost of something.
Sometimes it is a fixed amount.
'£5 discount is given if this bill is paid within fourteen days.'
This means that £5 is taken off the bill if you pay it before the fourteen days are up.
Often it is a ***percentage*** of the total.
10% discount means that you can take 10% of the price off the amount you pay.
$10\% = \frac{10}{100} = \frac{1}{10}$
If the price is £20, the 10% discount would be $\frac{1}{10}$ of £20.
The discount would be £2. You would pay £18.

distance

This tells us how far it is from one place to another; the length from one point to another. The shortest distance between two points is a straight line.

The international measurement of distance is based on the metre. In this country we sometimes measure in kilometres for longer distances but sometimes we still use miles.
km/h stands for kilometres per hour.
mph stands for miles per hour.

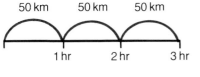

If you travel at 50 km/h you go 50 km in each hour.
If you travel for 3 hours at 50 km/h the distance you would cover would be (3×50) km $= 150$ km.

A man travels at 60 mph for 2 hr 15 min ($2\frac{1}{4}$ hr). What distance does he travel?

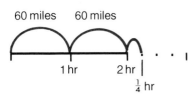

He travels 60 miles in every hour.
In 2 hours he travels (60×2) miles $=$ 120 miles
In $\frac{1}{4}$ hour he travels ($\frac{1}{4}$ of 60) miles $=$ 15 miles
In $2\frac{1}{4}$ hours he travels 135 miles

Time (in hours) $\times$ speed (in km/h) $=$ distance covered (in km)
Time (in hours) $\times$ speed (in mph) $=$ distance covered (in miles)

divide

To divide is to separate. When we talk about dividing in Maths we usually mean separating into equal groups or sharing out.
The sign for dividing is $\div$. We read it as 'divided by'.

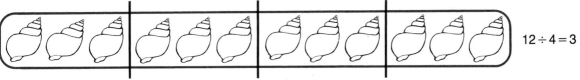

$12 \div 4 = 3$

If you want to know more, look up **division**.

divisibility tests

These are quick checks to see if one number will divide exactly into another number. They are useful if you are cancelling fractions, finding factors or dealing with problems where people or things are being sorted out into groups. (Will a number of people fit exactly into a number of coaches, for example, or will you have some spare seats?)

Unfortunately there isn't a simple test for every number but these are worth knowing:

2s Even numbers will always divide exactly by 2.
Even numbers end in 0, 2, 4, 6 or 8.

396 is an even number. It will divide exactly by 2.

$$\begin{array}{r} 198 \\ 2\overline{)396} \end{array}$$

3s Add up the digits of your number. If the answer will divide exactly by 3, then your number will too.

342   $3 + 4 + 2 = 9$,   9 divides exactly by 3

342 will divide exactly by 3.

$$\begin{array}{r} 114 \\ 3\overline{)342} \end{array}$$

4s If the last two digits of a number will divide exactly by 4, the whole number will.

3432   32 will divide exactly by 4.

3432 will divide exactly by 4.

$$\begin{array}{r} 858 \\ 4\overline{)3432} \end{array}$$

4 also divides exactly into 100 and any other number of whole hundreds.

5s 5 will divide exactly into any number ending in 5 or 0.

6s If you have an *even* number try the test for threes on it. An *even* number which will divide exactly by 3 will also divide exactly by 6.

9s Add up the digits of your number. If the answer divides exactly by 9 then your number will too.

432   $4 + 3 + 2 = 9$.

432 will divide exactly by 9.

$$\begin{array}{r} 48 \\ 9\overline{)432} \end{array}$$

10s If a number ends in 0 it will divide exactly by 10.

11s If your number has two digits they will be the same if they divide by 11 exactly. Think of the 11 × table. 22 33 44 55 and so on. If your number has three digits, the outside two added together make up the middle one.
1 3 2 $1 + 2 = 3$.   3 is in the middle.
4 5 1 $4 + 1 = 5$.   5 is in the middle.
1 5 4 $1 + 4 = 5$.   5 is in the middle.
8 8 0 $8 + 0 = 8$.   8 is in the middle.
All of these numbers would divide exactly by 11.

division

Division is dividing into equal groups or sharing. The sign we use is ÷. We read it as 'divided by'.
Division is the opposite of multiplication. When we multiply we collect up numbers of equal groups. When we divide we start with the whole collection and split it up into equal groups.

Multiplying

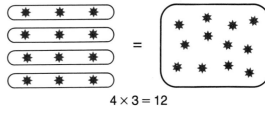

$4 \times 3 = 12$

Dividing

$12 \div 4 = 3$

We need to divide for all of the following examples.
Divide 10 people into 2 **equal groups**.

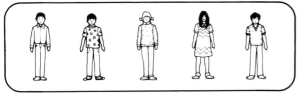

$10 \div 2 = 5$
There would be 5 in each group.

How many groups of three are there in 9?

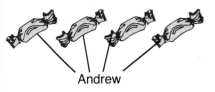  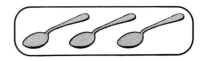

$9 \div 3 = 3$
There are 3 groups of three.

Share 12 sweets between 3 children.

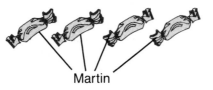

Andrew   Martin   Jason

$12 \div 3 = 4$
They could have 4 sweets each.

Partition 8 into 4 equal subsets.

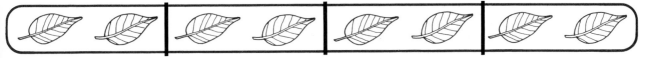

$8 \div 4 = 2$
There would be 2 in each subset.

Plant 15 cabbages in 3 equal rows. How many will be in each row?
You could take 3 cabbages and plant one in each row.

15 − 3 = 12. There are 12 still to plant.

Plant 3 more. There are 9 still to plant.

Plant 3 more. There are 6 still to plant.

Plant 3 more. There are 3 still to plant.

Plant 3 more. They are all planted.

There are 5 cabbages in each row.

This kind of dividing is called **repeated subtraction.**

Another way of doing this would be to divide the 15 cabbages into 3 groups. (One group for each row).

15 ÷ 3 = 5

There would be 5 cabbages in each group.
5 cabbages could be planted in each row.

Division can be written down like this:

12 ÷ 4 = 3   *or* $\dfrac{3}{4\sqrt{12}}$ or $4\underline{|12}$ *or* $\dfrac{12}{4} = 3$
                                      3

We say 'How many fours are there in 12?'

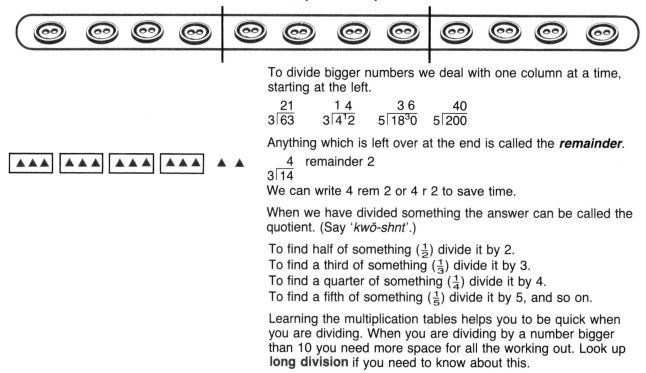

To divide bigger numbers we deal with one column at a time, starting at the left.

$\dfrac{21}{3\sqrt{63}}$ $\dfrac{1\ 4}{3\sqrt{4^12}}$ $\dfrac{3\ 6}{5\sqrt{18^30}}$ $\dfrac{40}{5\sqrt{200}}$

Anything which is left over at the end is called the **remainder**.

$\dfrac{4\ \ \ \text{remainder 2}}{3\sqrt{14}}$

We can write 4 rem 2 or 4 r 2 to save time.

When we have divided something the answer can be called the quotient. (Say '*kwō-shnt*'.)

To find half of something ($\frac{1}{2}$) divide it by 2.
To find a third of something ($\frac{1}{3}$) divide it by 3.
To find a quarter of something ($\frac{1}{4}$) divide it by 4.
To find a fifth of something ($\frac{1}{5}$) divide it by 5, and so on.

Learning the multiplication tables helps you to be quick when you are dividing. When you are dividing by a number bigger than 10 you need more space for all the working out. Look up **long division** if you need to know about this.

dodecagon

A flat shape with 12 straight sides and 12 angles.

A **regular dodecagon** has 12 equal sides and 12 equal angles.

regular dodecagon

dodecahedron

(The plural is **dodecahedra**.) This is a solid shape with 12 faces. If all the faces are exactly the same size and shape it is called a **regular dodecahedron** and each face will be a **regular pentagon**. (A pentagon is a flat five-sided shape.)

double

If you double something you make it twice as big. You multiply it by 2. If you have £5 and double your money you end up with £10 (2 × £5).

dozen

A dozen is 12. Half a dozen is 6. Two dozen is 24 (2 × 12). A gross is 12 dozen.

duodecimal

We all start off with a number system based on groups of ten – hundreds, tens and units and so on. Sometimes it is called the decimal system. The duodecimal system is a number system based on twelves.

Older people are more used to counting up groups of twelve because they used 12 pennies to make a shilling and 12 inches to make a foot. We do still count things in dozens sometimes. (1 dozen = 12) 12 dozen = 1 gross (144). Another name for the duodecimal system is base 12. Look up **bases** if you need to know about counting in different bases.

ellipse

An ellipse is an oval shape.
The earth goes round the sun in a path which is an ellipse.
When you draw a bowl or a cup you draw an ellipse for the top.
The top is **not** an ellipse, it only looks that way in the diagram.

empty set

An empty set is a set with no members. Nothing belongs to it. It is written { } or ∅.

equations

Equations are sometimes called mathematical sentences or number sentences. They always follow the same pattern. Whatever is on the left equals whatever is on the right.

$$3 + 6 = 9 \qquad 10 = 6 + 4 \qquad 3 \times 2 = 6 \times 1$$
$$14 \div 2 = 7 \qquad 7 - 3 = 8 - 4$$

These are all equations. Whatever comes before the equals sign (=) is worth the same as whatever comes after it.

Sometimes one of the numbers is missing. If you have to solve an equation you have to find the missing number.

$8 + \boxed{} = 10 \qquad \boxed{} - 4 = 2$

$8 + \boxed{2} = 10 \qquad \boxed{6} - 4 = 2$

Remember equations are like balancing scales. The amount on one side equals the amount on the other side. If you add something to one side you must add the same amount to the other side to keep them balancing. If you take something away from one side you must take the same amount from the other side to keep them balancing. It is the same with multiplying or dividing. Whatever you do to one side you must do to the other side.

You can use this to help you solve equations.

$3 + x = 7$

Take 3 from both sides and you will be left with x.

$$3 + x - 3 = 7 - 3$$
$$x = 4$$

equilateral triangle

Equilateral means having equal sides. An equilateral triangle has all three sides equal in length. The angles are all equal too.

equivalent

This means of equal value, **equi-val**ent. We use the equals sign, =. A £1 note is equivalent to 10 ten pence pieces. It is not exactly the same thing – it wouldn't be much use in a 10p slot machine – but it is of equal value.

$\frac{2}{4} = \frac{1}{2}$

$\frac{1}{2} = \frac{3}{6} = \frac{4}{8} = \frac{5}{10}$

These are all called equivalent fractions. They are of equal value. They are worth the same.

estimate

An estimate is a sensible guess.

even numbers

Even numbers are whole numbers which can be divided exactly by 2.

They are called even because they can always be put into pairs with no odd ones left over.

2 is an even number.

3 is an odd number. See its odd one!

4 is an even number

5 is an odd number. See its odd one!
Even numbers always end in 0, 2, 4, 6 or 8.

exterior

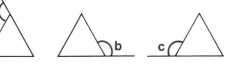

This means outside. The opposite is interior, meaning inside. The exterior angles of a triangle are outside the triangle. An exterior angle is formed by making one of the sides of the triangle longer so that it sticks out.

a, **b** and **c** are all exterior angles of the triangle.

external

This means outside. The external walls of a house are the outside walls. The opposite is internal, meaning inside.

factors

A factor is a whole number which will divide exactly into another whole number.
3 is a factor of 12 ($12 \div 3 = 4$).
4 is a factor of 12 ($12 \div 4 = 3$).
2 and 6 are factors of 12 as well.
$12 \div 2 = 6$ $12 \div 6 = 2$.
The factors of 20 are 2, 4, 5, 10 and 20.

Numbers which are multiplied together are factors of the answer.
$2 \times 4 = 8$
2 is a factor of 8   4 is a factor of 8.
When we are cancelling fractions we need to find a **common** factor.
This is the factor which is common to both of the numbers we are dealing with.

Look at $\frac{12}{15}$ 2 will divide exactly into 12 but not into 15.
3 will divide exactly into both 12 and 15.
3 is a common factor.
$\frac{\cancel{12}^4}{\cancel{15}_5} = \frac{4}{5}$

A **prime** factor is a factor which is also a prime number. It cannot be broken down into smaller equal groups.
  3 is a prime factor of 21
  7 is a prime factor of 21
$21 = 3 \times 7$.

Fahrenheit

Fahrenheit is the name of a kind of thermometer and its measuring scale.
The freezing point of water is marked at 32 degrees Fahrenheit (32°F).
The boiling point of water is marked at 212 degrees Fahrenheit (212°F).
Nowadays the **Celsius** (or centigrade) scale is used more often.
To convert (change) a Fahrenheit temperature to the Celsius scale, take 32° from the number of degrees Fahrenheit, then multiply your answer by $\frac{5}{9}$.

Temperature equivalents

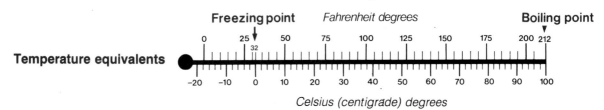

family tree

This is a chart to show how the members of a family are related to one another.

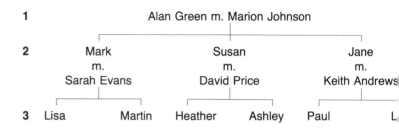

The family tree above shows three generations. Keep looking back at the family tree as you read about the people.

1 Alan Green married (m.) Marion Johnson. She became Mrs Green. They became the parents of Mark, Susan and Jane. They became the grandparents of Lisa, Martin, Heather, Ashley, Paul and Lucy.

2 Mark, Susan and Jane are the second generation on this family tree. They are the son and daughters of Alan and Marion Green. (Their surnames would be Green until the girls married.) Mark, Susan and Jane are brother and sisters to each other. They – and Mark's wife and Susan's and Jane's husbands – become the parents and aunts and uncles of the next generation. They have each started their own branch of the family tree.

3 Lisa, Martin, Heather, Ashley, Paul and Lucy are the third generation on this family tree. They are the grandchildren of Alan and Marion Green.
Paul and Lucy are brother and sister. They are the cousins of Lisa, Martin, Heather and Ashley. Paul and Lucy are the son and daughter of Jane and Keith Andrews. They are nephew and niece of Susan and David, Mark and Sarah.

On a family tree dates of birth and death are sometimes put in underneath each person's name (for example b.1920 d.1979 means born 1920 and died 1979).
If you need to work out how long it is from one date to another date the section on **dates** will help you.

feet, foot

An old style Imperial measure of length.
12 inches (in) = 1 foot
3 feet (ft) = 1 yard
1760 yards (yd) = 1 mile.
1 foot measures about 30 cm.

formula

(The plural is formulae.) In Maths a formula is a quick way of writing down a rule.

The formula for finding the area of a rectangle is $a = l \times b$.
a stands for the area of a rectangle
l stands for the length of the rectangle
b stands for the breadth (width) of the rectangle.

$a = l \times b$ (area of rect. = length × breadth)

$b = \frac{a}{l}$ (breadth of rect. = area ÷ length)

$l = \frac{a}{b}$ (length of rect. = area ÷ breadth)

The area of a triangle is half the base multiplied by the height.
This can be written as $\frac{1}{2}b \times h$ or $\frac{b \times h}{2}$

The volume of a cube or cuboid is $l \times b \times h$
(length × breadth × height).
This is the same as area of base × height.

The area of a circle = πr^2 ($\pi \times r \times r$)
π is about 3·14 or $3\frac{1}{7}$
r stands for radius.

The circumference of a circle = πd (π × the diameter)
This is the same as $2\pi r$ (2 × π × the radius)

A formula gives us a pattern for working something out.

fractions

Fractions are parts of something. The bottom number of a fraction is called the de**nom**inator. It is the **name** of the fraction and tells us the number of equal parts something has been divided into.
The top **number** of a fraction is called the **numerator**. It tells us how many of those parts we are dealing with.

numerator
denominator

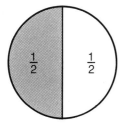

$\frac{1}{2}$ is called a half. It means that something has been divided into 2 equal parts or groups and we have one of them.
We have one piece out of the two. $\frac{1}{2}$.

$\frac{1}{2}$ is shaded
$\frac{1}{2}$ is unshaded

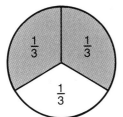

$\frac{2}{3}$ is called two thirds. It means that something has been divided into 3 equal parts or groups and we have 2 of them.
We have 2 pieces out of the three. $\frac{2}{3}$.

$\frac{2}{3}$ is shaded
$\frac{1}{3}$ is unshaded

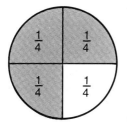

$\frac{3}{4}$ is called three quarters. Something has been divided into 4 equal parts or groups and we have 3 of them. We have 3 pieces out of the four. $\frac{3}{4}$.

$\frac{3}{4}$ is shaded
$\frac{1}{4}$ is unshaded

> If we need to find $\frac{1}{2}$ of something we divide it by 2
>
> If we need to find $\frac{1}{3}$ of something we divide it by 3
>
> If we need to find $\frac{1}{4}$ of something we divide it by 4
>
> If we need to find $\frac{1}{5}$ of something we divide it by 5
>
> and so on.
>
> To find $\frac{2}{3}$ of something, find $\frac{1}{3}$ of it then multiply by 2
>
> To find $\frac{5}{6}$ of something, find $\frac{1}{6}$ of it then multiply by 5
>
> To find $\frac{9}{10}$ of something, find $\frac{1}{10}$ of it then multiply by 9

Whole numbers

Two halves make one whole
Three thirds make one whole
Four quarters make one whole.

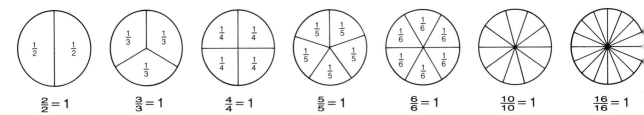

$$\frac{2}{2}=1 \qquad \frac{3}{3}=1 \qquad \frac{4}{4}=1 \qquad \frac{5}{5}=1 \qquad \frac{6}{6}=1 \qquad \frac{10}{10}=1 \qquad \frac{16}{16}=1$$

If the numerator and the denominator are the same, the fraction is equal to 1 whole one. Something has been divided up into a number of pieces and we have all of them

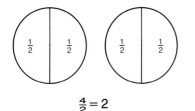

$$\frac{4}{2}=2 \qquad\qquad \frac{6}{3}=2 \qquad\qquad \frac{8}{4}=2$$

4 halves make up 2 whole ones.
6 thirds make up 2 whole ones.
8 quarters make up 2 whole ones.

Mixed numbers

A mixed number has both whole numbers and fractions.

$$2\frac{1}{2} \qquad 1\frac{7}{8} \qquad 12\frac{5}{6} \qquad 15\frac{2}{7}$$

These are all mixed numbers.

Improper fractions

These are sometimes called top-heavy fractions.
The numerator is more than the denominator.

$$\frac{5}{4} \qquad \frac{10}{6} \qquad \frac{12}{6} \qquad \frac{10}{3}$$

These are all improper fractions.
Improper fractions can be changed to **whole numbers** or **mixed numbers**.

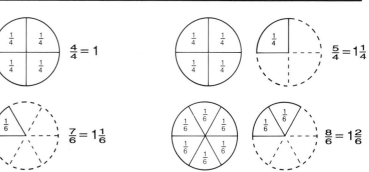

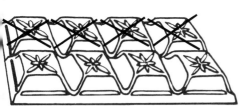

$$\frac{4}{4}=1 \qquad \frac{5}{4}=1\frac{1}{4}$$

$$\frac{6}{6}=1 \qquad \frac{7}{6}=1\frac{1}{6} \qquad \frac{8}{6}=1\frac{2}{6}$$

To change an improper fraction to whole or mixed numbers we can divide the numerator by the denominator. That will tell us how many whole numbers we can make up. If there are any remainders they will be the fractions that are left over.

$$\frac{10}{6}=1\frac{4}{6} \qquad \frac{12}{6}=2 \qquad \frac{13}{6}=2\frac{1}{6}$$

$$\frac{27}{5}=5\frac{2}{5} \qquad \frac{28}{5}=5\frac{3}{5} \qquad \frac{23}{10}=2\frac{3}{10}$$

Equivalent fractions

These are fractions of equal value. They are worth the same.

If you eat $\frac{4}{8}$ of a bar of chocolate you have eaten four pieces out of the eight. You have eaten half of it.

$\frac{4}{8}=\frac{1}{2}$ They are equivalent fractions.

$\frac{1}{2}=\frac{2}{4}=\frac{3}{6}=\frac{4}{8}=\frac{5}{10}$ and so on. These are all equivalent fractions.

To change a fraction to an equivalent fraction

If we multiply anything by 1 we do not change its value.
$3 \times 1 = 3 \qquad £5 \times 1 = £5$
If we multiply the numerator and the denominator of a fraction by the same number we do not change its value. It is the same as multiplying by $\frac{2}{2}$ or $\frac{3}{3}$ or $\frac{4}{4}$ and so on.

$$\frac{1}{2}=\frac{1\times4}{2\times4}=\frac{4}{8} \qquad \frac{1}{2}\times\frac{4}{4}=\frac{4}{8} \qquad \frac{1}{2}=\frac{4}{8}$$

$$\frac{3}{5}=\frac{3\times2}{5\times2}=\frac{6}{10} \qquad \frac{3}{5}\times\frac{2}{2}=\frac{6}{10} \qquad \frac{3}{5}=\frac{6}{10}$$

If you multiply the top number of a fraction by something you must multiply the bottom number by the same thing.

$$\frac{4}{6}=\frac{12}{\square} \qquad (4 \times \underline{3} = 12$$
$$6 \times \underline{3} = \boxed{18} \ )$$

$$\frac{4}{6}=\frac{12}{18}$$

The same thing happens if we divide by 1.
If we divide a fraction by $\frac{2}{2}$ or $\frac{3}{3}$ or $\frac{4}{4}$ and so on, we do not change its value.

$$\frac{15}{25}=\frac{3}{\square} \qquad (15 \div \underline{5} = 3$$
$$25 \div \underline{5} = 5)$$

$$\frac{15}{25}=\frac{3}{5}$$

If you divide the top number of a fraction by something you must divide the bottom number by the same thing.

Cancelling

We use cancelling when we divide the numerator and denominator of a fraction by the same number.

$$\frac{4}{16} = \frac{\cancel{4} \times 1}{\cancel{4} \times 4} = \frac{1}{4} \quad \text{or} \quad \frac{\cancel{4}^{1}}{\cancel{16}_{4}} = \frac{1}{4}$$

$$\frac{2}{8} = \frac{\cancel{2} \times 1}{\cancel{2} \times 4} = \frac{1}{4} \quad \text{or} \quad \frac{\cancel{2}^{1}}{\cancel{8}_{4}} = \frac{1}{4}$$

A number which will divide exactly into both the numerator and the denominator is a common **factor**. There are some hints about finding factors in the section on **divisibility tests**.

If you can find a common factor you can use cancelling to *simplify* a fraction or *reduce it to its lowest terms*. You can cancel out that common factor.

Reduce to its lowest terms (simplify)

To simplify a fraction or bring it to its lowest terms we bring the fraction down to the smallest, easiest numbers we can. We cancel as much as possible. We change improper fractions to whole or mixed numbers.

$$\frac{\cancel{18}^{6}}{\cancel{3}_{1}} = \frac{6}{1} = 6 \qquad \frac{10}{9} = 1\frac{1}{9} \qquad \frac{\cancel{14}^{7}}{\cancel{16}_{8}} = \frac{7}{8}$$

$$\frac{12}{10} = 1\frac{\cancel{2}^{1}}{\cancel{10}_{5}} = 1\frac{1}{5} \qquad \frac{\cancel{20}^{1}}{\cancel{100}_{5}} = \frac{1}{5}$$

Adding and subtracting fractions

It is easy to add and subtract fractions if they have the same denominator.

3 fifths + 1 fifth = 4 fifths

$$\frac{3}{5} \quad + \quad \frac{1}{5} \quad = \quad \frac{4}{5}$$

5 sixths − 4 sixths = 1 sixth

$$\frac{5}{6} \quad - \quad \frac{4}{6} \quad = \quad \frac{1}{6}$$

If we are dealing with different kinds of fractions we have to change them to the same sort before we can add or subtract them. We need to find a *common denominator*.

For $\frac{2}{5} + \frac{3}{10}$ 10 could be the common denominator.
5 will divide into 10 exactly
10 will divide into 10 exactly
Both fractions could be tenths.

$$\frac{2}{5} = \frac{\square}{10} \qquad 2 \times \underline{2} = 4$$
$$5 \times \underline{2} = 10$$

$$\frac{2}{5} = \frac{4}{10}$$

$\frac{3}{10}$ does not need to be changed.

$$\frac{2}{5} + \frac{3}{10}$$
$$= \frac{4}{10} + \frac{3}{10}$$
$$= \frac{7}{10}$$

To add or subtract fractions with a different denominator:

1 Add (or subtract) any whole numbers.

2 Change the fractions to fractions with the same denominator

3 Add (or subtract) the fractions.

4 Look at your answer. Can you cancel it? Is it an improper fraction? Make sure your answer is in its lowest terms.

$2\frac{1}{2} + 1\frac{7}{8}$ $\qquad\qquad$ $3\frac{2}{3} - 1\frac{1}{2}$
$= 3\frac{1}{2} + \frac{7}{8}$ $\qquad\qquad$ $= 2\frac{2}{3} - \frac{1}{2}$
$= 3\frac{4}{8} + \frac{7}{8}$ $\qquad\qquad$ $= 2\frac{4}{6} - \frac{3}{6}$
$= 3\frac{11}{8}$ $\quad(\frac{8}{8} = 1)$ $\qquad$ $= 2\frac{1}{6}$
$= 4\frac{3}{8}$

There is just one awkward thing that can happen to you when you are subtracting fractions. Look at this one:

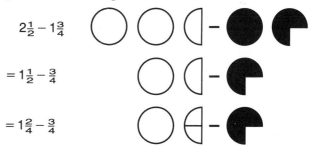

$2\frac{1}{2} - 1\frac{3}{4}$

$= 1\frac{1}{2} - \frac{3}{4}$

$= 1\frac{2}{4} - \frac{3}{4}$

Here is the awkward bit! We can't take $\frac{3}{4}$ away from $\frac{2}{4}$.
We have to break up the whole one. If it was a cake we would cut it up.
We need to change the whole one into quarters like the rest of the fractions. $1 = \frac{4}{4}$

$1\frac{2}{4} - \frac{3}{4}$
$= \frac{6}{4} - \frac{3}{4}$

$= \frac{3}{4}$

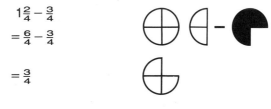

To change mixed numbers to improper fractions

Remember $1 = \frac{2}{2} = \frac{3}{3} = \frac{4}{4} = \frac{5}{5} = \frac{6}{6}$ and so on.

1 Look to see the kind of fraction you have.

2 Change your whole numbers to this kind of fraction. It may help you to think of them as whole cakes to be cut into equal pieces.

3 Add on the fraction you have and show how many pieces you have altogether.

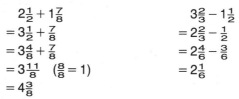

$2\frac{7}{8} =$

$2\frac{7}{8} = \quad \frac{8}{8} \quad + \quad \frac{8}{8} \quad + \quad \frac{7}{8} \quad = \frac{23}{8}$

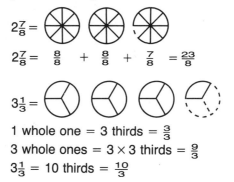

$3\frac{1}{3} =$

1 whole one = 3 thirds = $\frac{3}{3}$
3 whole ones = 3×3 thirds = $\frac{9}{3}$
$3\frac{1}{3} = 10$ thirds = $\frac{10}{3}$

To multiply fractions

1 Change any whole numbers or mixed numbers to improper fractions.

2 Cancel if you can. If you are multiplying you can cancel by dividing **any** numerator and **any** denominator. Remember you **must** divide them both by the same number.

3 Multiply across the top; multiply across the bottom.

4 Make sure your answer is in its lowest terms.

$$\frac{1}{4} \times \frac{1}{3} = \frac{1}{12}$$

$$2\frac{1}{2} \times \frac{4}{15}$$
$$= \frac{5^1}{2_1} \times \frac{4^2}{15_3}$$
$$= \frac{2}{3}$$

$$4\frac{2}{3} \times 1\frac{2}{7}$$
$$= \frac{14^2}{3_1} \times \frac{9^3}{7_1} = \frac{6}{1}$$
$$= 6$$

$$\frac{1}{2} \text{ of } \frac{5}{6} = \frac{1}{2} \times \frac{5}{6} \qquad \frac{5}{9} \text{ of } \frac{3}{4} = \frac{5}{9} \times \frac{3}{4}$$

To divide fractions

1 Change any whole numbers or mixed numbers to improper fractions.

2 Turn the fraction which comes after the division sign upside down and **multiply**.

(This is sometimes called multiplying by the inverse or multiplying by the reciprocal of the fraction.)

$$\frac{1}{16} \div \frac{1}{8}$$
$$= \frac{1}{16_2} \times \frac{8^1}{1}$$
$$= \frac{1}{2}$$

$$3\frac{1}{2} \div 1\frac{3}{4}$$
$$= \frac{7}{2} \div \frac{7}{4}$$
$$= \frac{7^1}{2_1} \times \frac{4^2}{7_1}$$
$$= \frac{2}{1}$$
$$= 2$$

Ordinary common fractions are sometimes called **vulgar fractions**. **Decimal fractions** are often just called decimals. There is a separate section under **decimals** to remind you about them.

function

A function is a connection between two sets. It is the same as a **mapping**. It connects every member of the first set to a member of the second set.

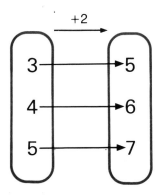

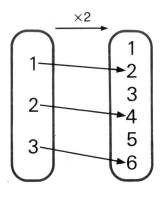

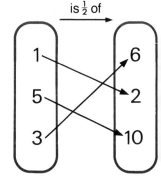

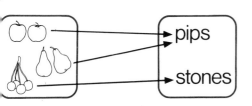

Each member of the first set has one – and only one – partner in the second set. Sometimes they do share a partner though.

Graphs are often drawn to show functions. The members of the first set are usually along the horizontal axis and the members of the second set are on the vertical axis.

geoboard

A geoboard is sometimes called a nailboard.

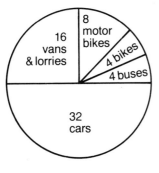

Elastic bands can be stretched over the nail-heads or knobs to make shapes quickly and compare them.

gram

(Sometimes spelt gramme.) This is the metric measure of mass.

1000 milligrams (mg) = 1 gram (g)
1000 grams = 1 kilogram (kg)
1000 kilograms = 1 tonne
1 kilogram is about 2·2 lbs in the old system of weighing.
28 grams are about 1 ounce (oz).

graphs

A graph is a special kind of chart or diagram. It shows a table of information clearly without using a lot of words or lists of figures. A simple way of doing this is to use a **pie chart**.

Pie chart

A pie chart looks like a pie marked off into slices.

Vehicles passing school between 10 a.m. and 11 a.m.

Pictogram

Look at this example:

Glasses of squash drunk at a party

Andrew	🥛🥛🥛
Jason	🥛🥛🥛
Richard	🥛🥛
Martin	🥛🥛🥛
Paul	🥛🥛🥛🥛
Ashley	🥛🥛🥛🥛🥛

🥛 stands for (represents) 1 glass of squash.

This can be called a *picture graph*, a *pictograph* or *pictogram*. Most people seem to call it a pictogram. The information is shown by a series of little pictures.

If you are drawing a pictogram make sure the title tells people what it is about. Choose a very simple little picture or symbol because you will have to draw a lot of them and they all have to be the same size and shape. Make sure all your symbols are above one another and in neat rows so that everyone can see your information at a glance. Always say what one symbol stands for.

If you are dealing with large numbers you can make one symbol stand for a lot.
Look at the next example:

40 people had arranged an outing to Windsor, 30 were going to Hampton Court, 60 were going to London and 25 were going to Bournemouth.

 represents (stands for) 10 people.

We wrote the place names down first before we started drawing – otherwise it would have been hard to get the symbols above each other.

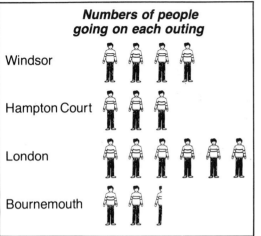

Numbers of people going on each outing

Windsor

Hampton Court

London

Bournemouth

stood for 10 people.   stood for 20 people

We needed to show 25 for Bournemouth. 5 is half of 10 so we had to draw half a symbol to stand for 5.

stood for 25.

Another way of drawing a pictogram is to use a horizontal and a vertical axis.

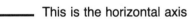

This is the vertical axis

This is the horizontal axis

The pictogram about squash at the party could have been drawn like this:

Glasses of squash drunk at a party

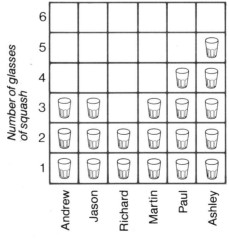

Number of glasses of squash

Andrew   Jason   Richard   Martin   Paul   Ashley

Boys at the party

A bar chart

This is a block graph or column graph where the information is shown in rows or bars. (See **bar charts** for more details.)

Line graph

We can show information by drawing lines instead of bars or blocks.
This is sometimes called a stick graph.

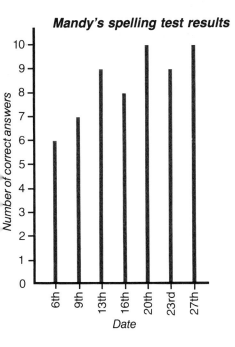

Mandy's spelling test results

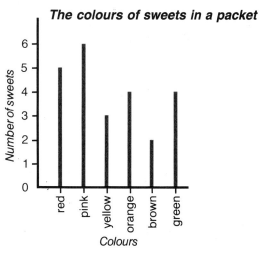

The colours of sweets in a packet

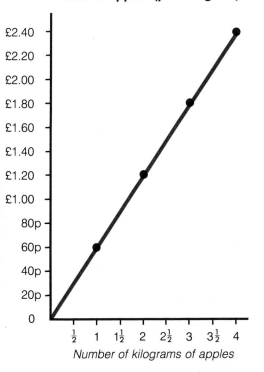

Cost of apples (per kilogram)

Sometimes only the points which would be at the top of each line are marked in or 'plotted'.

If these points are joined together we get a straight line. It is called a straight-line graph. Some graphs have curved lines. Some go up and down.

On this graph we can see at a glance that 1 kilogram of apples costs 60p and 2 kilograms of apples cost £1.20.
$1\frac{1}{2}$ kilograms of apples cost half way between those two amounts. We can read off in between amounts on this sort of graph.

When you are drawing a graph

It is easiest when you draw a graph to work on squared paper. Your paper may not be big enough for you to use one square for each thing you are counting. You may have to let each square stand for two or more. This is called using a smaller **scale**.

Remember

1 Use a sharp pencil.

2 Give a heading or title to tell people what your graph is about.

3 Fit your graph on to your page so that it is as easy to see and understand as possible. (Leave enough space to draw both axes.)

4 Label the axes so that people can understand your information.

Watch out for graphs in newspapers and advertisements.

gross

1 gross = 144
A gross is the name for 12 dozen (1 dozen = 12)
$$12 \times 12 = 144).$$
The word gross can also mean 'in total'.
The gross weight of a box of chocolates is the total weight of the box, and the paper and packing, as well as the chocolates inside. The net weight is just the weight of the chocolates.

HCF

This stands for highest common factor. A **factor** is a whole number which will divide exactly into another number.
3 is a factor of 12 $(12 \div 3 = 4)$
4 is a factor of 12 $(12 \div 4 = 3)$
2 and 6 are factors of 12 as well.
The highest common factor of two or more numbers is the largest number which will divide into them exactly.
The highest common factor of 12 and 18 is 6.
It is the largest number which will divide exactly into both of them.

half

(The plural is halves). If something is divided into two equal pieces or groups each part is called a half.
It can be written as $\frac{1}{2}$

To find half of something we divide it by 2. Two halves make up a whole one.
$$\frac{1}{2} + \frac{1}{2} = 1 \qquad \frac{2}{2} = 1$$
$$\frac{1}{2}\text{kg} + \frac{1}{2}\text{kg} = 1\text{kg} \quad 2 \times \frac{1}{2}\text{kg} = 1\text{kg}$$

halve

To halve something we divide it into two equal parts.

Each part is called a half.
If we need to halve a number or an amount of something we divide it by 2.

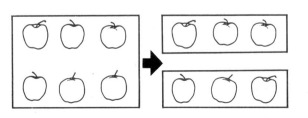
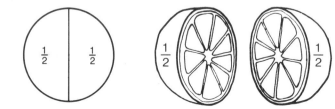

hexadecimal

Sometimes this is called 'hex' for short. It is another name for base 16.
The '*hex*' part of the word means six. (Think of *hex*agon.)
The *decimal* part means something to do with tens.
Base 16 is very useful to computer programmers. It gives them a short way of writing down long binary numbers.
If you want to know about counting in base 16 look up **bases**.

hexagon

A hexagon is a shape which has six straight sides and six angles.
If all the sides and angles are equal it is called a *regular* hexagon.

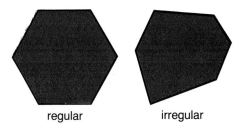

regular   irregular

hexagonal

Hexagonal means having six sides and six angles.

hexomino

A hexomino is a shape made from six squares.

horizontal

This means level, parallel to the horizon or the ground.
If you have a glass of water and tilt it, the surface of the water stays level.

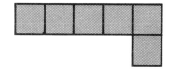

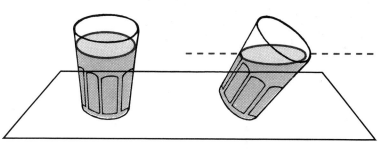

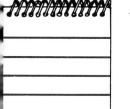

We say this is horizontal.
A table top should be a horizontal surface – level and flat.

If you are writing on a lined page the lines are horizontal.

If the book has squared pages it will have vertical lines going from top to bottom as well.

hour

60 seconds = 1 minute
60 minutes = 1 hour
24 hours = 1 day

> To change hours into minutes multiply by 60.
> To change minutes into hours divide by 60.
> To change hours into days divide by 24.
> To change days into hours multiply by 24.

There is more information under **time**, the **twenty-four hour clock** and **timetables**.

hypotenuse

The hypotenuse is the longest side of a right-angled triangle. It is the side opposite the right angle.

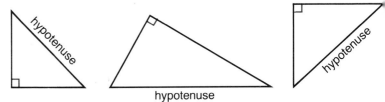

Imperial units

These used to be the standard measurements in Britain. We still use some of them. These are the ones you are most likely to meet:

Length	Capacity	Mass
12 inches (in) = 1 foot (ft) 3 ft = 1 yard (yd) 1760 yd = 1 mile	8 pints = 1 gallon	16 ounces (oz) = 1 pound (lb) 14 lb = 1 stone (st) 112 lb = 1 hundredweight (cwt) 20 cwt = 1 ton

If you want to know more, look up **capacity**, **pound**, **length** and **mass**.

improper fractions

These are sometimes called 'top heavy fractions'. The top number of the fraction is bigger than the bottom number.

$\frac{3}{2}$ $\frac{7}{4}$ $\frac{8}{4}$ $\frac{13}{10}$

These are all improper fractions.
If you need to know more look up **fractions**.

increase

To increase means to make more or to make bigger.
An increase is something which is added on.
We talk about an increase in weight, an increase in appetite, increasing the number of stitches in knitting, price increases, pay increases, population increases.
If you *increase* your score by 10, you *add* 10 on to it.
If a man gets a pay *increase* he earns more money – something is *added* on to his pay.

Increase 14 by 2
14 + 2 = 16.

index indices

(The plural of index is indices – say *in-diss-eez*.)
The index of a book is a list of subjects which people might want to look up. It gives the numbers of the pages where each subject can be found.
When we are dealing with numbers, index has a different meaning and it can be a real time-saver.
Look at these numbers multiplied by themselves.

$2 \times 2 = 2^2$

We can call this 2 squared or 2 to the power of 2. The little number in the air is called the index or the power.

$2 \times 2 \times 2 = 2^3$

We can call this 2 cubed or 2 to the power of 3. The index is 3.

$2 \times 2 \times 2 \times 2 = 2^4$

We can call this 2 to the fourth or 2 to the power of 4.
The index is 4.

$2 \times 2 \times 2 \times 2 \times 2 \times 2 \times 2 \times 2 \times 2 \times 2 = 2^{10}$

The index is 10 (count the number of 2s)

$5 \times 5 \times 5 \times 5 = 5^4$

The index is 4.

ingredients

The contents of a mixture. The ingredients of a cake are the exact amounts of flour, margarine, sugar, eggs and so on which go in to make that kind of cake.

integer

An integer is a whole number. It can be any of the whole numbers we use for counting including 0, positive numbers and negative numbers.

interior

Inside. The interior angles of a triangle are the three angles inside it.

The three interior angles of a triangle add up to 180°.

The opposite is exterior, meaning outside.

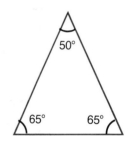

internal

Inside. The internal walls of a house are the inside walls. The opposite is external, meaning outside.

intersect intersection

If two lines intersect they cut across each other.

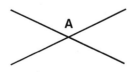

These lines intersect at A.   These arcs intersect at B.

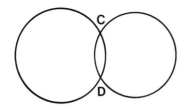

These circles intersect at C and D.

A, B, C and D are points of intersection – the points where lines cross each other.

Sets can intersect too.

C = {children in my road}
J = {children going to Judo club}
G = {children going to Gym club}
Bill and Ann go to both clubs. They are members of both sets, so the sets intersect.
The sign we use for the intersection of sets is ∩.
J ∩ G = {Bill, Ann}

inverse

If you turn something upside down or back to front in Maths you have its inverse. The inverse of $\frac{2}{3}$ is $\frac{3}{2}$.

invert

Means to turn upside down or back to front. If you invert a fraction the top number changes place with the bottom number $\frac{4}{6}$ inverted becomes $\frac{6}{4}$

isosceles

An isosceles triangle has two sides of equal length. It also has two equal angles.

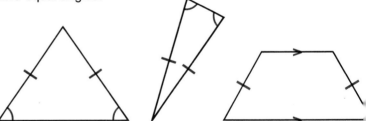

An *isosceles trapezium* has two sides of equal length. They are the sides which are not parallel.

kilo

Kilo comes from the Greek word for a thousand.

kilogram

(Sometimes spelt kilogramme.) A kilogram (kg) is a metric measure of mass or weight. 1 kilogram = 1000 grams (g). A kilogram is about 2·2 lbs (pounds).
If you want to know more about mass and weight, look up **mass**.

kilometre

A kilometre (km) is a metric measure of length.
1 kilometre = 1000 metres (m).
A kilometre is about $\frac{5}{8}$ mile (8 km are about 5 miles).

LCM

stands for lowest (or least) common multiple.
4, 6, 8, 10, 12 and so on, are all multiples of 2.
2 will divide exactly into any of them.
6, 9, 12, 15 and so on are all multiples of 3.
3 will divide exactly into all of them.

6 and 12 are common multiples of 2 and 3.
2 and 3 will divide exactly into both of them.
6 is the lowest common multiple because it is the smallest number that they will both divide into exactly. 6 is the LCM of 2 and 3.

24 is a common multiple of 2, 4 and 6 but 12 is the lowest common multiple. It is the smallest number that they will all divide into exactly. 12 is the LCM of 2, 4 and 6.

lattice

A lattice is a criss-cross pattern.
Lines are drawn across each
other leaving a network of spaces.

lattice multiplication

is a way of setting out long multiplication. It is explained in the section on **Napier's bones**.

leap year

A year is supposed to be the length of time the earth takes to go round the sun. In the time of Julius Caesar the calendar was redesigned to make it more accurate. The year became 365 days long with an extra day every fourth year – the leap year. Leap years have 366 days.

Leap years are the ones which will divide by four exactly, e.g. 1984, 1988, 1992, 1996 and so on. The extra day is February 29th. In other years February has only 28 days.

There is one more tiny complication. By 1582 Julius Caesar's calendar was about ten days out. Pope Gregory and his experts sorted out the problem and started the Gregorian calendar. Instead of counting *all* the centennial years (1600, 1700 and so on) as leap years, we now only count them as leap years if their first two figures divide exactly by four. 1600 and 2000 count as leap years. 1800 and 1900 count as ordinary years.

length

When you are measuring the length of something look at your ruler or tape measure carefully. Some have a blank piece at the end in case the corners get damaged. This bit is called the waste end. Make sure you start measuring from the beginning of the first centimetre (or inch).

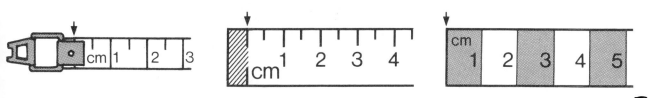

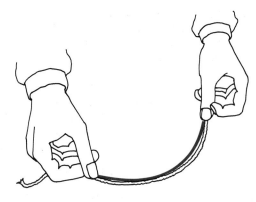

You can measure a curve with the help of a piece of thread.

Hold its end at the end of the line, then curve it on top of the line a little bit at a time. Nip the thread with your finger nails level with the other end of the line. Keep your nails nipped in the same place on the thread and pull it straight. Now move it to the ruler to measure. It will not give an accurate answer but if your are careful you should not be far out.

Use your sense to decide whether to measure in mm, cm, m or km and what to use. Metre sticks, a trundle wheel and surveyors' long tapes are useful for measuring longer distances. The metric measures of length are:

10 millimetres (mm) = 1 centimetre (cm)
10 centimetres (cm) = 1 decimetre (dm)
10 decimetres (dm) = 1 metre (m)
100 centimetres = 1 metre
1000 metres = 1 kilometre (km)

The Imperial measurements of length are:

12 inches (in) = 1 foot (ft)
3 feet (ft) = 1 yard (yd)
1760 yards = 1 mile

There are several more but you are not very likely to need them.

1 inch is about 2·5 centimetres
1 foot is about 30 centimetres
1 metre is about 39 inches (3 inches more than a yard)
1 kilometre is about $\frac{5}{8}$ mile
(8 km are about 5 miles)

less

This means fewer, not as many.
3 less than 5 is 2.

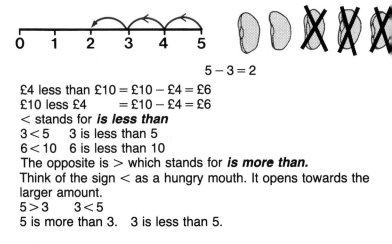

$5 - 3 = 2$

£4 less than £10 = £10 − £4 = £6
£10 less £4 = £10 − £4 = £6
< stands for **is less than**
3 < 5   3 is less than 5
6 < 10   6 is less than 10
The opposite is > which stands for **is more than.**
Think of the sign < as a hungry mouth. It opens towards the larger amount.
5 > 3   3 < 5
5 is more than 3.   3 is less than 5.

lines

You should have a good point on your pencil whenever you draw a line because really it should have no width at all! It has only one measurement and that is its own length. There are hints about measuring straight lines and curved lines in the section on **length**.

You might need to look up some of the following sections for information on different kinds of lines: **diagonal**, **diagonals**, **graphs** (for line graphs), **horizontal**, **oblique**, **parallel**, **perpendicular**, **symmetry** (for lines of symmetry), **vertical**.

litre

We can buy litres of wine, litres of fizzy lemonade, litres of petrol and so on. A litre is an amount of liquid.

We can also measure the amount of liquid that a container can *hold* in litres. This is called a measure of *capacity*.

1000 millilitres (ml) = 1 litre (l)

The plastic teaspoon the chemist gives with a bottle of medicine holds 5 millilitres (ml). Sometimes cubic centimetres are used for measuring small quantities.

$$1000 \text{ cubic centimetres (cm}^3) = 1 \text{ litre (l)}$$
$$1 \text{ cubic metre (m}^3) = 1000 \text{ litres.}$$

1 litre is about $1\frac{3}{4}$ pints. $4\frac{1}{2}$ litres are about 1 gallon (8 pints).

long division

We can use long division when we are dividing by a number bigger than 10. If you are not sure about dividing by smaller numbers look up **division** and read that through carefully first. This section won't teach you how to do long division, but it might help you to remember about it if you have forgotten.

With ordinary division we use the *multiplication tables* to find how many groups of a certain size we can make out of a larger number.

$3 \times 6 = 18$ How many 3s are there in 18? 6

How many 6s are there in 18? 3

With long division we have to work out the table first.

$$\begin{array}{r} 2 \\ 21\overline{)42} \end{array} \qquad 1 \times 21 = 21 \\ \phantom{21\overline{)42} \qquad} 2 \times 21 = 42$$

We deal with bigger numbers in long division. Working out how many are left over is sometimes awkward to do in your head. Long division is a way of setting down a division sum so that all the working out can be neatly done on paper.

(The little r stands for remainder. It means left over.)

$$\begin{array}{r} 3\text{ r }19 \\ 21\overline{)82} \\ -63 \\ \hline 19 \end{array} \qquad \begin{array}{l} 2 \times 21 = 42 \\ 3 \times 21 = 63 \\ 4 \times 21 = 84 \end{array}$$

In the next one we have an extra bit to deal with.

$$\begin{array}{r} 12\text{ r }1 \\ 21\overline{)253} \\ -21\downarrow \\ \hline 43 \\ -42 \\ \hline 1 \end{array} \qquad \begin{array}{l} 2 \times 21 = 42 \\ 3 \times 21 = 63 \end{array}$$

Instead of putting the 4 which is left over up next to the 3 as we would in ordinary division, we bring the 3 down beside the 4. This gives us space to work out the next bit.

Remember to keep your columns of figures straight so they don't get muddled up with each other.

```
       218 r 18      2 × 21 = 42
21 ⟌ 4596            3 × 21 = 63
       42↓           9 × 21 = 189
       39|           8 × 21 = 168
       21↓
      186
      168
       18
```

(We know $1 × 21 = 21$ and $10 × 21 = 210$ so we can work out the parts of the table we think we might need. We don't **have** to work out the whole table.)

long multiplication

We can use long multiplication when we are multiplying by numbers more than 10. If you are not sure about multiplication with numbers below 10 look up **multiplication** first and read it carefully.

When we need to multiply by numbers more than 10 our tables don't go far enough and it is very awkward to manage in one line of working. What we do is to split it up into bits we can manage and do a bit at a time. Long multiplication is no more difficult than ordinary multiplication – it just goes on a bit longer.

For $32 × 14$ we work out $32 × 10$
and $32 × 4$
and add the two results together.
(Remember the easy way of multiplying by 10, shown on page 35.)

```
   32        32        320
 × 10       ×  4      + 128
  320       128        448
```

There is a neat way of setting this out.

```
    32
 ×  14
   320      (This row is 32 × 10)
 + 128      (This row is 32 × 4)
   448      (This row is 32 × 14)
```

To multiply 146 by 24
we work out $146 × 20$
and $146 × 4$
and add the results together.

```
    146
 ×   24
   2920     (This row is 146 × 20)
 +  584     (This row is 146 × 4)
   3504     (This row is 146 × 24)
```

Do remember to keep your rows and columns straight or you will get muddled up.
This section will not teach you how to do long multiplication – you must ask for help if you need it – but it should remind you what it is if you have forgotten.

loss

If a shopkeeper buys something for 30p and sells it for 25p he has made a loss. He is worse off than when he started.
He spent 30p
He received 25p
His loss was 5p (30p − 25p).

mph

stands for miles per hour. 30 mph means a speed of 30 miles per hour.
If you travelled at 30 mph for two hours you would have gone 60 miles. (30 miles in each hour.)

magic squares

In a magic square the numbers in any row, column or diagonal add up to the same total.

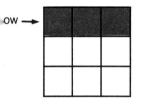
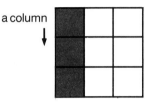
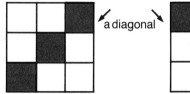
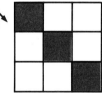

You can make a magic square of any size as long as you have an odd number of columns and rows. These are magic squares:

6	1	8
7	5	3
2	9	4

9	2	7
4	6	8
5	10	3

12	5	10
7	9	11
8	13	6

In the first one every row, column and diagonal adds up to 15. In the second each one adds up to 18. In the third each one adds up to 27. Check and see for yourself.

mapping

1 When we are mapping out a journey we are planning a route. We might be finding the road which connects two towns.

2 Mapping in Maths is a connection between two **sets**. A mapping links every member of the first set with a member of the second set. It is the same as a **function**.

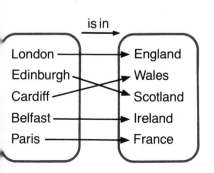
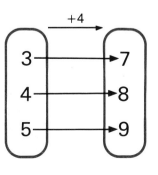
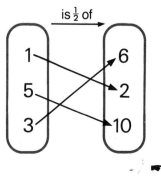

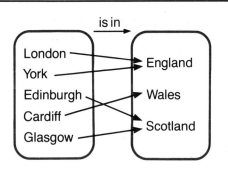

Each member of the first set has one, and only one, partner in the second set. Sometimes they do share a partner though.

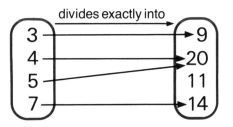

Graphs are often drawn to show mappings. The members of the first set are usually along the horizontal axis and members of the second set are on the vertical axis.

mass

Some Maths books use the word *mass* where we might expect the word *weight*. Some use both words. There is a difference between the two.

The mass of a person's body is the amount of matter in it.

The weight is a measure of the amount of pull on that body by gravity.

We talk about an astronaut being 'weightless' when he has escaped from the pull of earth's gravity, but his mass has not changed. He is the same man with the same insides and the same clothes.

A lunar module has the same mass on Earth as it has on the moon.

The pull of the moon's gravity is much less than the pull of earth's gravity though.

It takes much less thrust to get the lunar module off the moon's surface than it does to get it off the earth's surface. It seems lighter but it has the same mass, wherever it is.

Normally all this does not affect our daily lives.

We weigh things for cookery, we buy our fruit and vegetables by weight, we check our weight on the bathroom scales, and we use one of the following tables:

Imperial measure
16 ounces (oz) = 1 pound (lb)
14 pounds = 1 stone (st)
112 pounds = 1 hundredweight (cwt)
20 cwt = 1 ton

Metric measure
1000 milligrams (mg) = 1 gram (g)
1000 grams (g) = 1 kilogram (kg)
1000 kg = 1 tonne

We might sometimes need:
100 grams = 1 hectogram
10 hectograms = 1 kilogram
To mathematicians and scientists, though, the difference between mass and weight is very important.

matrix
matrices

(The plural of matrix is matrices – say *may-trix, may-triss-eez*.)
A matrix is a mould where something is shaped. It is also the name for a rectangular pattern where numbers or symbols are arranged. If you are asked to 'complete the matrix', use the information you have been given to fill in the spaces in the rectangle.

$14 \times 13 = 182$

Complete the matrix

Number	14	14	140
Number	1·3	0·13	13
Product			

(Remember the product is the answer when you have multiplied.)
We are told that $14 \times 13 = 182$, so we can use that information and fill in the spaces in the matrix without much trouble.

Number	14	14	140
Number	1·3	0·13	13
Product	18·2	1·82	1820

Here are the results of some netball matches:

Team	Won	Drew	Lost
St Peter's	5	0	5
St Mary's	5	3	2
St Andrew's	4	2	4
St Anne's	3	1	6

This information can be written as a matrix:

$$\begin{pmatrix} 5 & 0 & 5 \\ 5 & 3 & 2 \\ 4 & 2 & 4 \\ 3 & 1 & 6 \end{pmatrix}$$

maximum

The highest possible amount; the largest possible size or quantity.
A maximum thermometer shows the highest temperature which has been reached in a certain time. (The opposite is minimum).

mean

The mean is the *average* amount. If you want to know more, look up **average**.

median

A median is a straight line drawn from the tip of an angle of a triangle to the middle of the opposite side.

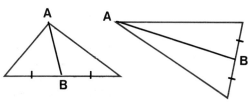

AB is a median.

metre

The standard metric measure of length.

10 millimetres (mm) = 1 centimetre (cm)
100 centimetres (cm) = 1 metre (m)
1000 metres = 1 kilometre (km)

A metre is just over 39 inches in the Imperial system of measuring.

The word metre really means a measure and any word with -metre- in it has something to do with measuring.

metric

The metric system is a measuring system. The basic units are: the metre for measuring **lengths**, the litre for measuring **capacity** and the gram for measuring **weight** (or **mass**).

There is a section on each of these in this book. In the metric system all the units are arranged in tens and tens of tens. These are the most useful ones to know:

Length	
	10 millimetres (mm) = 1 centimetre (cm)
	100 centimetres = 1 metre (m)
	1000 metres = 1 kilometre (km)

Mass	
	1000 grams (g) = 1 kilogram (kg)
	1000 kilograms = 1 tonne
	You might need:
	1000 milligrams (mg) = 1 gram
	100 grams = 1 hectogram
	10 hectograms = 1 kilogram

Capacity	
	1000 millilitres (ml) = 1 litre (l)

Area	
	100 square millimetres (mm^2) = 1 square centimetre (cm^2)
	10000 square centimetres = 1 square metre (m^2)
	10000 square metres = 1 hectare (ha)

If you want to know how to change from one unit of measurement to another (inches to m, kg to pounds and so on) look up **convert** .

mile

An Imperial measure of distance – or length.

1760 yards = 1 mile.

mph stands for miles per hour.

30 mph means a speed of 30 miles per hour.

1 kilometre (the metric measure of length or distance) is about $\frac{5}{8}$ mile.

(8 kilometres are about 5 miles.)

milli-

Words beginning with milli- have something to do with a thousand.

Milligram

A milligram is a metric measure of **mass**.
1000 milligrams (mg) = 1 gram (g)

Millilitre

A millilitre is a measure of **capacity** in the metric system.
1000 millilitres (ml) = 1 litre (l)

Millimetre

A millimetre is a measure of **length** in the metric system.
1000 millimetres (mm) = 1 metre (m)
10 millimetres = 1 centimetre (cm)

million

A million is a thousand thousands. It is written 1 000 000 (sometimes 1,000,000).
It is $10 \times 10 \times 10 \times 10 \times 10 \times 10$ which can be written as 10^6.

minimum

The minimum is the least possible amount; the lowest possible; the smallest possible. A minimum thermometer shows the lowest temperature that has been reached in a certain time. The opposite is maximum.

minus

The minus sign is −. It means less or 'take away'.
If you come home minus your plimsolls you come home without them.
If a man arrives at the station minus his wallet, he hasn't got it any more.

10 minus 4 means 10 − 4
£5 minus £2 means £5 − £2

(If you want to know about 'minus numbers' look up **directed numbers**.)

minute

A measure of time.
60 seconds = 1 minute
60 minutes = 1 hour
If you want to know more, look up **time**.

mixed numbers

A mixed number is a whole number with a fraction.
$3\frac{1}{2}$ $4\frac{5}{8}$ $7\frac{9}{10}$ are all mixed numbers.
Mixed numbers can be changed to improper fractions. This is useful for multiplying or dividing by fractions. Look up **fractions** if you have forgotten about this.

money

100 pence (p) = £1.
We can write 105p as £1.05
110p as £1.10
150p as £1.50 and so on.
We can write fifty pence as 50p or £0.50.
We can write five pence as 5p or £0.05.
The decimal point separates the pounds from the pence. There are always two figures after the point.

Coin	Number to make up £1
1p	100
2p	50
5p	20
10p	10
20p	5
50p	2

The sections on **bills** or **change** may be useful to you.

multiples

Multiples are collections of equal groups.
2 4 6 8 10 12 and so on are all multiples of 2.
2 will divide exactly into any of them.
5 10 15 20 25 30 and so on are all mutliples of 5.
5 will divide exactly into any of them.
LCM stands for *lowest common multiple*.
Look up **LCM** if you need to know about it.

multiplication

Multiplication is a quick way of adding up equal groups. The sign for multiplication is ×.
$2 + 2 + 2 + 2 + 2 + 2 + 2 + 2 = 16$

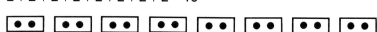

There are 8 groups of 2 here. 8 twos.
It is quicker to write $8 \times 2 = 16$.

If you have 4 packets of lollipops with six in each packet you could say you have $6 + 6 + 6 + 6$ altogether –
or even   6
            6
            6
          $+ 6$
          ——

It is quicker to say 4×6

If you had nine rows of cabbages with 12 cabbages in each row you could count them all up to see how many you had altogether. You could work out
12 + 12 + 12 + 12 + 12 + 12 + 12 + 12 + 12 cabbages
or 9 × 12

A multiplication table is a list of equal groups already counted up.

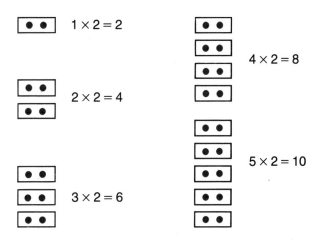

$1 \times 2 = 2$

$2 \times 2 = 4$

$3 \times 2 = 6$

$4 \times 2 = 8$

$5 \times 2 = 10$

That is how the 2 × table is built up.
The 3 × table counts up groups of three.

$1 \times 3 = 3$

$2 \times 3 = 6$

$3 \times 3 = 9$ and so on.

The 4 × table counts up groups of four.

It really is worth while learning the multiplication tables. Once you know them you can save yourself lots of time and trouble for the rest of your life. Know them backwards and forwards and dodging about. When you really know them your brain can punch out the answers faster than your fingers can use a calculator. Your brain doesn't need batteries either!

multiply

To multiply is to increase something a number of times. Multiplying is multiplication. Read the section above this if you want to know more details. It is all about multiplication.

Multiply 4 by 3 means 4 × 3
4 multiplied by 3 is 4 × 3

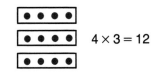

$4 \times 3 = 12$

Napier's bones

This is a way of doing long multiplication. It is named after John Napier. He was a Scottish mathematician (1550–1617). He invented ways of working things out. He used strips of wood and bone with grids and scales marked on them.

This is his way of multiplying 14 × 32 step by step.
First draw a grid.

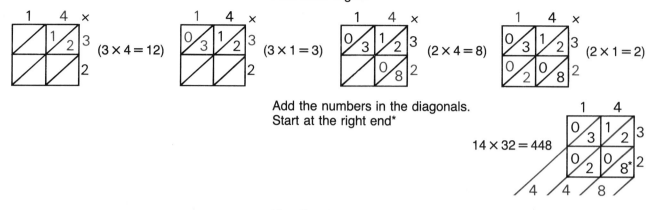

(3 × 4 = 12) (3 × 1 = 3) (2 × 4 = 8) (2 × 1 = 2)

Add the numbers in the diagonals.
Start at the right end*

14 × 32 = 448

Usually all the working out is done in one frame like these:

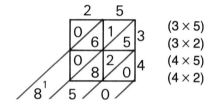

(3 × 5)
(3 × 2)
(4 × 5)
(4 × 2)

25 × 34 = 850

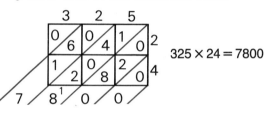

325 × 24 = 7800

negative numbers

A number with a minus sign before it is called a negative number.
A temperature of −5°C means that the temperature is 5°C below zero (freezing point.) −1 is one less than 0.

A number with a plus sign before it is called a positive number.
If there is no sign before a number it is always counted as positive.
Look up **directed numbers** if you want to know more.

net

There are two meanings to this word in Maths. They are quite different.
1 If you look at tins and packets of foodstuffs in the larder you will find 'net weight' somewhere on most of the labels. Net weight means the weight of whatever is inside not counting any packing or padding.

If you buy a tin of biscuits the net weight is the weight of the actual biscuits you are getting for your money. It does not include the weight of any fancy papers or cardboard separating the layers inside or the weight of the tin itself.

After a school fête someone might say 'The net profit was ... so much.'
The net profit is the amount of money they actually have in hand after they have paid all the expenses of running the fête. They might have paid for hiring a hall, for prizes, for tea and milk and sugar and so on. When all the money was counted up at the end of the fête, that would be called the **gross** profit. When all the expenses had been paid for, the money which was left would be called the **net** profit.

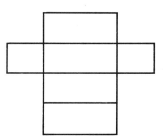

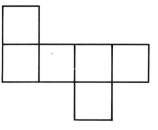

2 The other meaning of the word *net* is a kind of pattern. It is a flat shape which can be cut out and folded up to make a solid shape with length and width and height.

That is a net for making a cube.

You can see what the base will be. The sides are joined on to the base. The top is joined on to one side.

These nets would also make cubes.

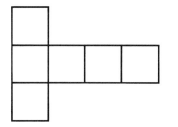

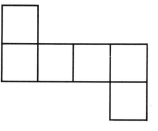

There are several other ways of drawing a net to make a cube.

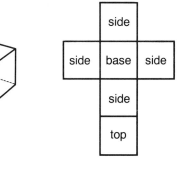

This net would make a cuboid.

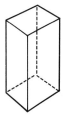

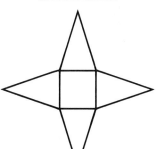

This net would make a pyramid.

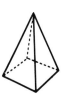

Sometimes little pieces are added on to nets. They make flaps which can be folded over and stuck on to another side.

nomogram
nomograph

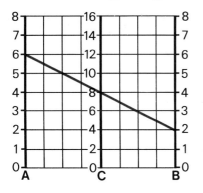

A nomogram (or nomograph) is a chart using three parallel lines. By putting a ruler across two of them some information can be read off the third one. This can save a lot of working out.

The nomogram on the left is for simple adding and subtracting.

To add any number in line A to any number in line B, put a ruler across joining the two numbers. The answer will be on line C just where the ruler crosses it.

The line is drawn on the diagram for 6 + 2. It crosses line C at 8.

To subtract any number in line B from any number in line C, put your ruler right across the lines and join the two numbers. The answer will be on line A just where the ruler crosses it.

The line drawn on the diagram shows 8 − 2 = 6.

noughts

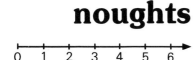

A nought is written as 0. It means none. 0 is also called zero. 0 can be a starting point in measuring or on a number line.

Noughts are very important in our number system. They are used to keep the numbers in their places.

	Th	H	T	U
3 is worth 3 units				3
30 is worth 3 tens			3	0
300 is worth 3 hundreds		3	0	0
3000 is worth 3 thousands	3	0	0	0

We can tell what the 3 is worth by its place. The noughts keep it in its place when there aren't any other numbers to do it. Really a nought in a column just means 'we haven't got any of these'.

301 means 3 hundreds, no tens and 1 unit
3 hundred and one.
310 means 3 hundreds, 1 ten and no units
3 hundred and ten.

Remember

	Th	H	T	U
		1	0	1
	1	0	0	1

101 is 1 hundred and 1.

1001 is 1 thousand and 1.

100 is 1 hundred
1 000 is 1 thousand (10 × 100)
10 000 is 10 thousand (10 × 1 000)
100 000 is 1 hundred thousand (10 × 10 000)
1 000 000 is 1 million (10 × 100 000)

If anything is multiplied by nought the answer is always nought.
5 × 0 = 0.
There is more detailed information about using noughts in the section on **decimals**.
There may be some information which is useful to you in the section on **bases** if you have been dealing with different bases.

number bases

Our usual way of counting is in sets of ten. We sometimes call it hundreds, tens and units. It is also called **base 10**. When we are working with numbers we always work in base 10 unless we are told something different.

It is possible to work with any number as a base. A word or a figure low down beside a number tells us which base it is in.
2_{five} or 2_5 means 2 in base 5.
2_{eight} or 2_8 means 2 in base 8.
If you don't remember about this look up **base**. It tells you all about counting in different bases.
Binary is a special name for base 2.
Hexadecimal or 'hex' is a special name for base 16.
The **decimal system** is base 10.
The **duodecimal system** is base 12.

numerals

Another word for numbers.

numerator

The numerator is the top number of a fraction. It tells us the number of pieces or parts we are dealing with. The bottom number of a fraction is called the **denominator**.

oblique

Slanting, sloping.

These are oblique lines.

obtuse angles

These are angles of more than 90° but less than 180°.

If you want to know more, look up **angles**.

octagon

An octagon is a flat shape with eight straight sides.

It is called a regular octagon if all its sides and angles are equal.

regular octagon   irregular octagon

octagonal

Having eight straight sides.

odd numbers

Odd numbers are whole numbers which will not split up into two exactly.
If you make them into pairs one odd one is always left over.

1 is an odd number

3 is an odd number.
It makes up one pair and has an odd one left over.

5 is an odd number.
See its odd one!

Odd numbers always end in 1, 3, 5, 7 or 9.
21 is odd. 365 is odd. 4169 is odd.

All the numbers ending in 0, 2, 4, 6 or 8 are called **even numbers**. They will all divide by 2 exactly.

odometer

An odometer is an instrument for measuring the distance a vehicle has travelled.

ordered pairs

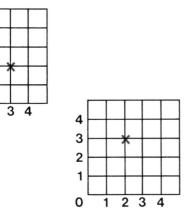

Sometimes it is important that numbers are put in a certain order. When we are dealing with pairs of numbers which must go a certain way round we call them ordered pairs. **Co-ordinates** are ordered pairs. (3, 2) means three along and two up.

The cross is at (3, 2)

(2, 3) does not mean the same thing. It means 2 along and 3 up.

The cross is at (2, 3)

(2, 3) and (3, 2) are ordered pairs. The numbers in each pair must be put in the right order. Ordered pairs are often plotted on graphs.

$\square \times 5 = \triangle$

(2, 10) is an ordered pair which could make that number sentence true.
2 could go in the first empty place ($\square$) and 10 could go in the second empty place ($\triangle$).
$2 \times 5 = 10$.
It would not make sense if the 10 and the 2 were put the other way round.
(There are many, many ordered pairs which would make that number sentence true (3, 15), (4, 20), (5, 25). You could go on finding them forever!)

ounce

Ounces are still used sometimes for weighing although they are part of the old **Imperial system**.

16 ounces = 1 pound
oz is short for ounce
lb is short for pound.

These pounds have nothing to do with money.

$12\,oz = \frac{3}{4}\,lb$
$8\,oz = \frac{1}{2}\,lb$
$4\,oz = \frac{1}{4}\,lb$

One ounce weighs about 28 grams in the metric system.

p.m.

Stands for **post meridiem**. It is Latin for after midday, afternoon.
5 p.m. means 5 o'clock in the afternoon.
5 a.m. (**ante meridiem**) means 5 o'clock in the morning. Look up **time** if you need more information.

parabola

If you hit a ball or throw something through the air it always goes in a curve.

This curve is called a parabola.

parallel lines

Parallel lines are the same distance apart from each other all the way along their length. Even if you make them longer they will never meet.

Often they are shown on diagrams
with little arrow heads
marked on them like this:

parallelogram

A parallelogram is a four-sided shape with its opposite sides parallel to each other.

partitioning

Another name for sharing or dividing. Partitioning a set means dividing it into subsets.

pentagon

A pentagon is a flat shape with five straight sides. If all the sides and angles are equal it is called a regular pentagon.

regular pentagon   irregular pentagon

pentomino

A shape made from five squares.

 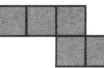 

percentages

Per **cent** means for every **hundred** or out of a hundred. The sign for per cent is %.

Here are 100 squares.
3 squares out of the hundred are shaded. $\frac{3}{100}$ are shaded.
$\frac{3}{100}$ can be called 3 per cent. It can be written as 3%.
3% of the squares are shaded. 97 of the squares are not shaded.
$\frac{97}{100}$ are not shaded.
$\frac{97}{100}$ can be called 97 per cent.
It can be written as 97%.
3% of the squares are shaded.
97% of the squares are unshaded.

$\frac{1}{100} = 1\%$ $\frac{2}{100} = 2\%$ $\frac{3}{100} = 3\%$ $\frac{24}{100} = 24\%$ $\frac{36}{100} = 36\%$
$\frac{74}{100} = 74\%$

A fraction with a **denominator** (bottom number) of 100 is called a percentage.

A boy had 56% for Maths. This means that he had 56 marks out of 100.
$56\% = \frac{56}{100}$

If someone had 100% it would mean that he had $\frac{100}{100}$. He had no mistakes at all.
$100\% = \frac{100}{100}$ 100% is the whole lot.

$50\% = \frac{50}{100} = \frac{1}{2}$ $25\% = \frac{25}{100} = \frac{1}{4}$ $75\% = \frac{75}{100} = \frac{3}{4}$

It is easy to write percentages as fractions.
$10\% = \frac{10}{100} = \frac{\cancel{10}^1}{\cancel{100}_{10}} = \frac{1}{10}$

$20\% = \frac{20}{100} = \frac{\cancel{20}^1}{\cancel{100}_5} = \frac{1}{5}$

It is useful to learn these as we often need them:

$75\% = \frac{3}{4}$ $33\frac{1}{3}\% = \frac{1}{3}$ $20\% = \frac{1}{5}$
$50\% = \frac{1}{2}$ $66\frac{2}{3}\% = \frac{2}{3}$ $10\% = \frac{1}{10}$
$25\% = \frac{1}{4}$ $5\% = \frac{1}{20}$
12.5% or $12\frac{1}{2}\% = \frac{1}{8}$ $1\% = \frac{1}{100}$

It is also useful to learn these decimals as percentages:
$0{\cdot}75 = 75\%$ $0{\cdot}1 = 10\%$
$0{\cdot}5 = 50\%$ $0{\cdot}01 = 1\%$
$0{\cdot}25 = 25\%$
$0{\cdot}125 = 12{\cdot}5\%$

Examples
Here are some examples of using percentages:

1 What is 10% of £20?
$10\% = \frac{10}{100} = \frac{1}{10}$
$\frac{1}{10}$ of £20 = £2.

2 Find 20% of 30 people.
$20\% = \frac{\cancel{20}^1}{\cancel{100}_5} = \frac{1}{5}$
$\frac{1}{5}$ of 30 people = 6 people.

3 In a sale 5% is taken off the usual price of everything in a window.

$5\% = \frac{5}{100} = \frac{1}{20}$

If the usual price of something is £40, $\frac{1}{20}$ of £40 is taken off.

$\frac{1}{20}$ of £40 = £2

£2 is taken off the usual price.

The sale price is £38 (£40 − £2).

4 Some employees are to have a 6% wage increase. How much rise will someone earning £4000 a year have?

A 6% rise means that for every £100 they earn they will get an extra £6:

On £100 they will get £6

On £1000 they will get £60

On £4000 they will get £60 × 4 = £240.

5 Members of a club are offered 10% discount. This means that 10% is taken off their bills. (Remember $10\% = \frac{1}{10}$). If a bill comes to £100, £10 is taken off. They pay £90. If a bill comes to £50, £5 is taken off. They pay £45.

6 A girl had $\frac{16}{20}$ for Maths, $\frac{15}{25}$ for English and $\frac{6}{10}$ for History. If you change all her marks to percentages it is easier to compare them.

To write a fraction as a percentage, change the fraction to one with a denominator (bottom number) of a hundred.

Maths $\quad \frac{16^{(\times 5)}}{20_{(\times 5)}} = \frac{80}{100} = 80\%$

English $\quad \frac{15^{(\times 4)}}{25_{(\times 4)}} = \frac{60}{100} = 60\%$

History $\frac{6^{(\times 10)}}{10_{(\times 10)}} = \frac{60}{100} = 60\%$

7 17 children out of 20 eat sandwiches at schools in one district. Write the number eating sandwiches as a percentage.

$\frac{17^{\times 5}}{20_{\times 5}} = \frac{85}{100} = 85\%$

If you have difficult numbers you can change your fraction to a percentage by multiplying it by 100. Express $\frac{3}{8}$ as a percentage.

$\frac{3}{8} \times \frac{100}{1} = \frac{300}{8} = 37\frac{4}{8} = 37\frac{1}{2}\%$

If you knew that $\frac{1}{8} = 12\frac{1}{2}\%$ you could say

$$\frac{3}{8} = 3 \times 12\frac{1}{2}\% = 37\frac{1}{2}\%$$

perimeter

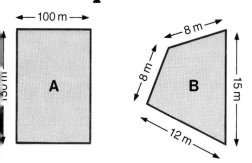

The perimeter is the distance all the way round the edge of something: the boundary.

A is a rectangular field.

Its perimeter = (100 + 150 + 100 + 150) metres

The perimeter = 500 metres.

B is a garden.

Its perimeter = (8 + 15 + 12 + 8) metres

The perimeter = 43 metres.

The perimeter of a circle is called the ***circumference***.

perpendicular

A line which is perpendicular to another one meets it at *right angles*.

Angle ABC is a right angle.
Angle ABD is a right angle.
AB is perpendicular to CD.

pi

Pi is a Greek letter. It is written as π. In Maths it is used to stand for a particular number which can't be worked out exactly. It is very nearly 3·142 or $3\frac{1}{7}$.
The **circumference** of a circle $= \pi d$ (π multiplied by the **diameter** of the circle.)
This comes to the same as $2\pi r$ ($2 \times \pi \times$ the radius of the circle.
The area of a circle $= \pi r^2$ ($\pi \times r \times r$)

pictogram

A pictogram or pictograph is a kind of *graph* which uses little pictures to show its information.

Here is a pictogram to show the glasses of squash drunk at a party.

Heather

Lisa

Karen

Hayley

Melanie

Mandy

Nicki

stands for 1 glass of squ

Altogether 22 glasses of squash were drunk. Hayley and Melanie drank the least. They had 2 glasses each. You can find quite a lot of information from a graph.
If you would like some hints on drawing pictograms look up the section on **graphs**. The part you need is near the beginning.

pie chart

A pie chart looks like a pie cut into slices. It is a way of showing information.

People travelling on a coach outing.
We can see very quickly that half of the people on the coach outing were women and that there were not nearly as many men.
$\frac{1}{8}$ of the people were men
$\frac{3}{8}$ were children.

Pie charts make it easy to compare amounts or shares.

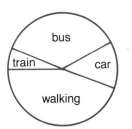

Transport used by children to get to school.

How Mark spent his pocket money.

Here the pie is divided into equal shares. It makes it easier to see how much each share stands for.

Mark had £1.60 pocket money.

$\frac{1}{16}$ of his money was saved.

$\frac{1}{16}$ of £1.60 = 10p

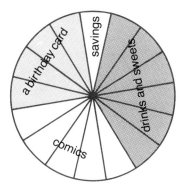

$\frac{6}{16}$ of his money was spent on drinks and sweets.

$\frac{6}{16}$ of £1.60 = 60p

$\frac{5}{16}$ of his money was spent on comics.

$\frac{5}{16}$ of £1.60 = 50p

$\frac{4}{16}$ of his money was spent on a birthday card.

$\frac{4}{16}$ of £1.60 = 40p

When you know how much pocket money Mark had you can work out all the rest of the information from the chart. You can compare the amounts he spent on different things just by looking at the chart.

When you are drawing a chart of your own you need to decide how big to make the slices.

The whole pie stands for the whole amount you are dealing with.

It is easy to divide a circle into halves, quarters, eighths, sixteenths and so on. Each slice is called a **sector** of the circle.

Sometimes the amounts you want to show don't divide into easy shares like that.
A circle can be divided up into 360°.
If the slices you need will divide exactly into 360° you can still make a pie chart.

Think of a class of 36 children.
The 360° of the circle would be divided between the 36 children. They would have a 10° slice each.

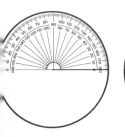

You could use this to make a pie chart about any subject to do with the class.

If you wanted a chart about favourite TV programmes you could ask for each child's favourite programme and colour in the right number of slices for each programme. Each programme would need a different colour to make it show up well. You always need to label charts so that other people can understand what they mean.

There is one difficulty with pie charts. Just suppose that the class had 39 children in it. Think about dividing up the circle then! If you don't have easy numbers to deal with you will find it better to draw a **bar chart** instead!

pint

Pints are a measure of capacity in the **Imperial system**. Pints are still used to measure some liquids.

8 pints = 1 gallon

1 pint is just over half a litre.

place value

The value of something is what it is worth.

H T U

    4   4 is worth 4 units.

  4 0   40 is worth 4 tens (no units).

4 0 0   400 is worth 4 hundreds (no tens, no units).

We can tell what the 4 is worth by its place.

3 4 8 2   The 3 is worth 3 thousands

              The 4 is worth 4 hundreds

              The 8 is worth 8 tens

              The 2 is worth 2 units.

If you are not sure what a number is worth put the headings above the figures:

Th H T U

1 0 4 2   is 1 thousand and forty-two.

              The 1 is worth 1 thousand

              The 0 shows there are no hundreds

              The 4 is worth 4 tens

              The 2 is worth 2 units.

Notice   Th H T U

                  1 0 1

              1 0 0 1

  101 is 1 hundred and 1

1001 is 1 thousand and 1.

If you want to know about place value when you have a decimal point to deal with, look up **decimals**.

plan

A plan is drawn as though you are directly above something, looking down. It is often called a bird's eye view.

This is a plan of a garden. ⟶

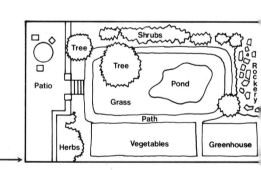

Sometimes it is not possible to label everything on the plan. Numbers or symbols can be used and a key shows what they stand for.

Usually a plan cannot be drawn life-size. It has to fit on to a piece of paper. Everything has to be smaller than it is in real life. If a plan is drawn to *scale* it means that everything on it has been carefully measured and made smaller in the same

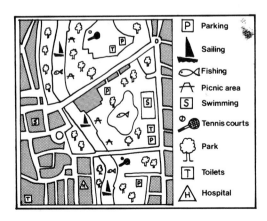

P	Parking
⛵	Sailing
🐟	Fishing
⛺	Picnic area
S	Swimming
🎾	Tennis courts
🌳	Park
T	Toilets
H	Hospital

way. If something which is 1 metre long is drawn as 1 centimetre long we say 1 cm represents 1 m. On that scale something which measures 2 metres in real life would be drawn 2 centimetres long. Something measuring $\frac{1}{2}$ metre in real life would measure $\frac{1}{2}$ centimetre on the plan.

Plans give an idea of the shapes and sizes of things and their positions. They can help us to find our way, to design a garden, to arrange the furniture in a room or to give directions. They can show us how the rooms of a house are arranged. They have very many uses. When we compare different plans, though, we must always look at the scale so that we can work out what the real life sizes or distances are. The plan for a dolls' house could be the same size as a plan for a real house! The section on **scale** may help you.

plane

A flat surface. It can be vertical, horizontal or oblique (sloping).

plot
plotting

In Maths this means marking points on a chart or a graph. When you are plotting your results you are marking them in on a chart or a graph instead of leaving them in a list.
A navigator may plot a course or a route.

plumb-line

A plumb-line is very useful for checking that something is exactly upright (vertical). A piece of string with a weight tied on one end will make a plumb-line. Hold the other end still. When the string stops swinging it will be hanging straight down. The string will be a vertical line.

plus

The plus sign is +. It means add.
7 plus 4 means 7 + 4.

polygon

Poly comes from the Greek word meaning many. The 'poly' bit in any word means many; **gon** comes from the Greek word for angles.

A polygon is a flat shape with 'many angles'. If all the angles and sides are equal it is called a regular polygon.
A three-sided polygon is called a triangle. There are several kinds of triangle so look up **triangles** if you want to know more about them. A four-sided polygon is called a quadrilateral. There are several kinds of quadrilateral, so look up **quadrilateral** if you want more details about these.

Mostly when we talk about polygons we are talking about shapes with more than four sides. Here are some of the special names which you might meet:

Pentagon a 5-sided polygon
Hexagon a 6-sided polygon
Heptagon a 7-sided polygon
Octagon an 8-sided polygon
Nonagon a 9-sided polygon
Decagon a 10-sided polygon
Dodecagon a 12-sided polygon

polyhedron

Polyhedron means 'many faces'. A polyhedron is a solid shape with many faces. (The plural is polyhedra.)

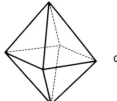
octahedron

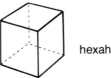
hexahedron

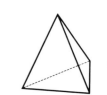
tetrahedron

A corner point where faces meet is called a **vertex**. (The plural is vertices.)

If each face is exactly the same size and shape the polyhedron is called a regular polyhedron. There are only five kinds of regular polyhedra:

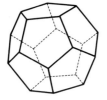
dodecahedron

Tetrahedron which has 4 faces. (Each face is an equilateral triangle.)

Hexahedron which has 6 faces – we usually call this a cube. (Each face is a square.)

Octahedron which has 8 faces. (Each face is an equilateral triangle.)

Dodecahedron which has 12 faces. (Each face is a regular pentagon.)

icosahedron

Icosahedron which has 20 faces. (Each face is an equilateral triangle.)

Deltahedra are polyhedra with equilateral triangles as their faces. A tetrahedron is one.

pound

A pound can be money or can be a measure of weight in the **Imperial system**.

Money £(pound)

100 pence = £1.00 The decimal point separates the pounds from the pence.

$75p = £0.75 = £\frac{3}{4}$
$50p = £0.50 = £\frac{1}{2}$
$25p = £0.25 = £\frac{1}{4}$
$20p = £0.20 = £\frac{1}{5}$
$10p = £0.10 = £\frac{1}{10}$
$5p = £0.05 = £\frac{1}{20}$
$1p \doteq £0.01 = £\frac{1}{100}$

There are always two figures after the decimal point.
One pound fifty pence is written as £1.50.
One pound five pence is written at £1.05.

Weight lb (pound)

Although we use the **metric** system for most things now, sometimes you come across old-fashioned scales marked in pounds and ounces and cookery books where the recipes are in pounds and ounces. These pounds are written as lb for short. Ounces are written oz for short.
16 oz = 1 lb   14 lb = 1 stone
I don't suppose you will need 14 lb of anything in a recipe, but many bathroom scales are marked in stones and pounds and you might want to weigh yourself!

To convert (change) ounces to grams, multiply by 28·35.
To convert pounds to grams, multiply by 453·6.
To convert pounds to kilograms, multiply by 0·4536.
It is usually near enough to count 1 oz as 28 grams and 1 lb as 450 grams.

population

The people who live in a place are called its population.
The population figures show the number of people living in a place.
The total population means all the people counted up.

positive numbers

Numbers which are greater than zero (0) are called positive numbers.

$$-5 \quad -4 \quad -3 \quad -2 \quad -1 \quad 0 \quad +1 \quad +2 \quad +3 \quad +4 \quad +5$$
←———negative numbers——→—|—←—positive numbers———→

Numbers which are less than zero are called negative numbers and they are written with a minus sign in front of them −1 −2 −3.

Numbers with a plus sign before them are called positive numbers. Numbers with no sign in front of them are always counted as positive. If you need to know more about positive and negative numbers, look up **directed numbers**.

powers

A power shows the number of times a number is to be multiplied by itself.

2^4 means $2 \times 2 \times 2 \times 2$

It is called 2 to the fourth or 2 to the power of 4. The little 4 in the air is the power.

2^5 means $2 \times 2 \times 2 \times 2 \times 2$

It is called 2 to the fifth or 2 to the power of 5. The little 5 in the air is the power. Another name for the power is the **index**.

prime numbers

Prime numbers are the awkward ones like 11, 17, 23 which don't break up into smaller equal groups.

You won't find them in the answers to your multiplication tables anywhere except when they are multiplied by 1.

They will only divide exactly by themselves and 1.

Examples of prime numbers are: 2, 3, 5, 7, 11, 13, 17, 19, 23, 29.

9 is not a prime number because it will split into three equal groups of three ($3 \times 3 = 9$).
11 is a prime number because however you try to split it into equal groups, you have something left over. You can only have one group of eleven (1×11) or eleven ones (11×1).

1 is not counted as a prime number. It is a special case because $1 \times 1 = 1$.

prism

A prism is a special kind of solid shape. Its two ends are exactly the same size and shape and they are parallel to each other. A prism is the same size and shape all the way through its length. It doesn't get thicker or thinner.

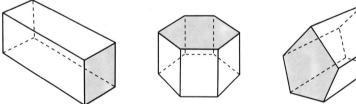

If you slice through a prism parallel to one of its ends, the new ends and the old ends will be exactly the same size and shape.

You may use glass triangular prisms in science lessons.

problems

If we call something a problem it sounds difficult before we start. This is a pity because it makes a lot of people afraid to use their common sense.

When we learn to count we can work out small problems in the home. How many knives and forks do we need when we are laying the table? How many more will we need if a visitor comes? Have we got enough chairs at the table? How many children are coming to the party? Parties can involve a lot of counting.

When we want to know 'how many?' we find that we have to count. As we get older we learn more about numbers and more about words and we can deal with more of these real life 'problems'.

Maths can be a quick way of writing down and sorting out these problems. We might write: 'We have five chairs in the dining room and three chairs in the kitchen. Altogether we have eight chairs.'

A Maths sentence is less chatty but much quicker. We would write:
5 chairs + 3 chairs = 8 chairs
5 + 3 = 8 is a Mathematical sentence. It is less work than writing it all out in words.

Sometimes when people look at a problem written out like a story, they look at the words, and think, 'it's Maths!' Then they pick out all the numbers and wonder what sort of sum to put them into. They don't give themselves a chance to get into the story.

Don't just look at the words. Read each sentence carefully. You are in charge. You are there. Picture it all happening. Think what you would do if you had to deal with this problem in real life. Often drawings will help you to see what you are doing.

Here is a problem:
A van delivered 4 parcels to a school. One held 144 books, one held 72 books and the other two held 36 books each. How many books were delivered altogether?

$$= \text{4 parcels of books}$$

$$
\begin{array}{r}
144 \\
72 \\
36 \\
36 \\
\hline
288 \\
\end{array}
$$

Altogether there were   288 books

There is often more than one way of working out a problem.

Five cars can each take 4 passengers. How many people can be given a lift?

4 passengers   4 passengers   4 passengers   4 passengers   4 passengers

Here are 5 cars. Put 4 passengers in each car.
4 + 4 + 4 + 4 + 4 = 20
or
5 × 4 = 20
20 people could be given a lift.

If you wanted to you could draw 4 people in each car and count them all up. It would take longer but you could still get the right answer.

If a problem seems difficult it often helps to give yourself the same problem with easy numbers. Think what you do with the easy numbers, then do the same thing to the bigger numbers.

If John had 28 more conkers he would have 150.
How many has he?

Try smaller numbers.
If John had 8 more conkers he would have 10.
How many has he?
There are lots of ways of doing this. Here is one way.

Here are ten conkers:

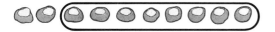

John has less than 10 conkers.
He has 8 less than 10 conkers.
He has $10 - 8$.
He has 2 conkers.
Now look at the problem we started with.
If John had 28 more conkers he would have 150.
How many has he?
John has less than 150 conkers.
He has 28 less than 150 conkers.
He has $150 - 28$.

$$\begin{array}{r} 150 \\ -28 \\ \hline 122 \end{array}$$

He has 122 conkers.

Some problems are more like puzzles. You can use an empty box in the place of a number you don't know.
If I multiply a certain number by 6, the answer is 54. What is the answer if I multiply the same number by 8?
The first sentence means

$\square$ (the number we don't know) $\times 6 = 54$
$\square \times 6 = 54$

$9 \times 6 = 54$
The 'certain number' must be 9.
Now look at the second sentence again:

If I multiply 9×8 the answer is 72.

Sometimes a problem seems difficult because you are not sure what some of the words mean or how they are used. **Look them up**.

A lot of words you might need are in this book. There are reminders of how the words are used and examples of problems in many of the sections. It might be helpful to read the section on **diagrams** too.

Remember

1 Read carefully. Check up on the words.

2 Draw a quick diagram or pictures to help you see what you are doing. Label everything you can.

3 Give yourself easy numbers if you are stuck.

If you are still stuck, write down everything you **do** know. Write in short Maths sentences underneath each other. Each sentence in your list is a clue. See what you can find out from each one. See if you can add anything to your diagram or pictures. Be a detective!

Don't be afraid to tackle 'problems' – and don't be afraid to ask for help if you need it. That's what we do with our real-life problems after all, isn't it? We do what we can ourselves and then we call in the experts!

product

The answer when something has been **multiplied**:
$4 \times 6 = 24$
The product of 4 and 6 is 24.

profit

If we buy something for £2 and sell it for £3 we say we have made a profit of £1. The profit is the extra money. It is the amount we have gained.

program

In this country we spell a television programme, a theatre programme and so on as progra**mme**.
A computer **program** is spelt without the extra **me** on the end. A computer program is a list of instructions which the computer can understand.

proportion

Sometimes two things are connected. When we are shopping, the more we buy the more we pay.

If we buy 1 packet of biscuits for 20p
       2 packets would cost $2 \times 20p$
       3 packets would cost $3 \times 20p$
       4 packets would cost $4 \times 20p$
       and so on.

We would say the amount we pay is in proportion to the number of packets.

Results like these are sometimes plotted on a graph.
If we are drawing a plan to scale we might draw a line 1 cm long to represent 50 cm in real life. We would draw a line of
$\frac{1}{2}$ cm to represent 25 cm ($\frac{1}{2}$ of 50)
1 cm to represent 50 cm
2 cm to represent 100 cm
and so on.

The two measurements may change but the proportion stays the same. Each real-life measurement is 50 times the measurement on the plan.
Two dots like this **:** are a sign we sometimes use when we are dealing with proportion.

☞

We could write:

plan measurement to real-life measurement = 1 to 50
or 1 : 50

Here is another example.
One boy worked for 1 hour and another boy worked for 4 hours. Share £10 between them in proportion to the hours they worked.

It would not be fair to pay them the same. One boy worked 4 times as long as the other one. He should be paid 4 times as much. We could call them Boy A and Boy B.

Boy A's hours : Boy B's hours : Total hours worked.
=   1   :   4   :   5
£10 ÷ 5 = £2. £2 could be paid for one hour's work.

Boy A would get £2.
Boy B would get £2 × 4 = £8.
That would use up the £10 fairly. The boys would be paid in proportion to the time they had worked.
You might find it helpful to look up the word **ratio**.

There is another way of working out proportion problems which is useful to remember. Some people call it 'finding one first'.
If 3 bags cost £15, what is the cost of 2 bags?
First find the cost of 1 bag. Next multiply by 2 to find the cost of 2 bags.
3 bags cost £15
1 bag costs £15 ÷ 3 = £5
2 bags cost £5 × 2 = £10

8 men would take 10 days to finish a job.
How long would it take if 10 men did it instead?

First find how long 1 man would take. (Don't forget that he would take longer on his own.) Next, share the work out between 10 men.
8 men take 10 days.
1 man would take 10 × 8 days = 80 days.
10 men would take 80 ÷ 10 days = 8 days.

protractor

A protractor is used for drawing and measuring angles. The sizes of the angles are marked in degrees.

Protractors can be circular or semi-circular. A semi-circular protractor is probably easier to handle to start with – and it is less likely to get broken in your pencil case. Transparent plastic ones are very cheap. If you get one with a picture on it, it may look more fun but the picture may hide a bit of the line on your page.

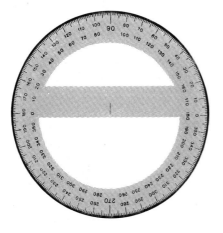

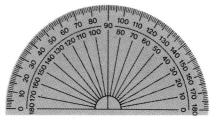

There are two scales marked on protractors. One goes from left to right and the other starts at the right and comes back to the left. This means that we can measure angles facing either way.

Measure the angle at B (∠ ABC)

1 Find the base line on the protractor. (It will be marked 0° 180° at both ends.)

2 Put the middle of the base line exactly on the tip of the angle at B.

3 Let the left-hand end of the base line run along on top of the line CB.

4 Hold the protractor still.

5 See where the line BA meets the scale on the protractor. Here, the **outer** scale shows the size of the angle. (Follow it round from the left end 0°.)

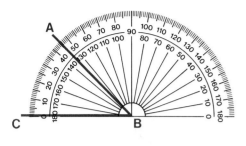

Sometimes we have to make the arm of the angle a bit longer so that it reaches the scale on the protractor. This doesn't change the size of the angle. It doesn't open it any wider or close it up.

Measure the angle at E (∠ DEF)

1 Find the base line again.

2 Put the middle of the base line exactly on the tip of the angle at E.

3 Let the right-hand side of the base line run along on top of the line EF.

4 Hold the protractor still.

5 See where the line ED meets the scale on the protractor. Here the **inner** scale shows the size of the angle. (Follow it round from the right end 0°.)

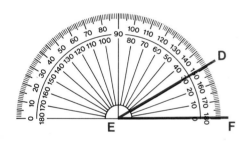

If you are muddled by the two scales, and don't know which answer is right, look at the size of your angle. See if it is more than a right angle (90°) or less. Then you should be able to choose the sensible answer.

Don't try to measure an angle upside down – turn your page round so that it is easy to manage.

pyramid

A pyramid is a solid shape. Its sides are triangles. These meet in a point at the top. This is called the **apex**. The base is a **polygon** – usually a square or a triangle.

triangular pyramid

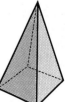

square pyramid

quadrant

A quarter of a circle.

The angle at the centre of the circle is a right angle.

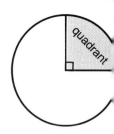

quadrilateral

A quadrilateral is a shape with four straight sides. Its four angles add up to 360° (degrees). Some quadrilaterals have special names.

A square

A square has four equal sides. Each of its angles is a right angle (90°).

A rectangle

Each angle of a rectangle is a right angle. Its opposite sides are of equal length and they are parallel to each other.

A parallelogram

A parallelogram has two pairs of parallel sides. Its opposite sides are equal in length.

A rhombus

A rhombus has four equal sides. The opposite sides are parallel. It looks like a square which has had a push!

A trapezium

A trapezium is a quadrilateral which has a pair of parallel sides.

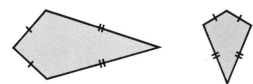

A kite

A kite has two pairs of adjacent sides which are equal in length. (Adjacent means next to each other.)

quadruple

To multiply by four. (Double it, and then double it again.) Four times the number.

quarter

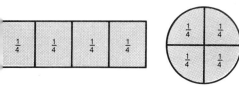

If something is divided into four equal pieces or groups each part is called a quarter.

It can be written as $\frac{1}{4}$.

To find a quarter of something we divide it by 4. Four quarters make up a whole one.

$\frac{1}{4} + \frac{1}{4} + \frac{1}{4} + \frac{1}{4} = 1$

Two quarters = a half. $\frac{1}{4} + \frac{1}{4} = \frac{1}{2}$

Three quarters is written $\frac{3}{4}$. $\frac{1}{4} + \frac{1}{4} + \frac{1}{4} = \frac{3}{4}$

A quarter of an hour ($\frac{1}{4}$ hr) is 15 minutes.
To quarter something is to cut it into four equal parts.

quotient

(Say *kwō-shnt*.) The number of times one number can be divided into another.
$10 \div 5 = 2$
The quotient is 2.
$11 \div 5 = 2$ remainder 1
The quotient is 2 and the remainder is 1.

radius
radii

(The plural of radius is radii.) The radius is the distance from the centre of a circle to its circumference (the edge).
To draw a circle with a radius of – say – 3 centimetres, the point of your pencil and the point of your compasses must be exactly 3 centimetres apart.

All radii of the same circle are equal.
There is more information
which might be useful to you in the
sections on **compasses** and **circle**.

ratio

One way of comparing things is to write them down as a ratio. We see how many times one amount divides into the other and then we can write down the ratio of one to the other.
The ratio of 4p to 12p
= 4 to 12
= 1 to 3

We can use this sign : to stand for 'to' or 'is to'.
The ratio of 5 apples to 10 apples
= 5 : 10
= 1 : 2

Remember that both amounts must be the same kind of thing before we can write them as a ratio. With 50p to £1 we change the £1 to 100 pence.
  50p : 100p
= 50 : 100
= 1 : 2

If we have a ratio like 4:6 we would write it as 2:3 not $1:1\frac{1}{2}$.
2:3 is easier to deal with. We always write a ratio as simply as we can.

Sometimes we need to share something out or divide it up in a certain ratio.

Say we had to share £10 in the ratio of 2:3 between Sue and Jane. The ratio 2:3 tells us that Sue is to have 2 shares and Jane is to have 3 shares.
We have £10 to be divided into 5 shares
£10 ÷ 5 = £2.
Each share is worth £2.
This means that Sue will have 2 × £2 = £4.
　　　　　　　　Jane will have 3 × £2 = £6.
We could write this
　 Sue : Jane : Total shares
= 2　:　3　:　　　5
£10 ÷ 5 = £2. One share = £2
Sue has 2 × £2 = £4
Jane has 3 × £2 = £6.

When some amounts are being compared and they have equal ratios we say they are in proportion. If you want to know more, look up **proportion**.

rectangle

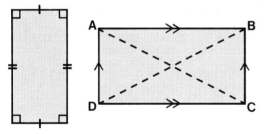

A rectangle is a quadrilateral. That means it is a shape which has four straight sides. Its angles are all right angles.
Its opposite sides are equal to each other in length. They are parallel.

The diagonals of a rectangle are equal.
AC = BD

To find the area of a rectangle we multiply its length by its breadth (width).
To find the perimeter of a rectangle we add up the length of all its sides.

rectangular numbers

If a number of dots can be arranged in a rectangle we say it is a rectangular number.

6 is a rectangular number
It can be arranged as
3 rows of 2 or 2 rows of 3.
3 × 2 = 6　　2 × 3 = 6

5 can't be arranged as a rectangle.

A straight line is not a rectangle.
5 is not a rectangular number.

15

No prime number can be a rectangular number.
All even numbers above two must be rectangular numbers.
Examples of rectangular numbers are 4, 6, 8, 9, 10, 12, 15.
A square is a special kind of rectangle.

reduce

To reduce something is to make it less. If the price of something is reduced it is made lower. If we reduce our weight we lose some weight. We weigh less.

If the price of a £5 book was reduced by £1 we would pay £4 for it. £1 would be taken off its price.

If the usual price of something is £1.50 and the sale price is £1 the reduction is 50p. It is the difference between the two prices.

If something is reduced by – say – 5 per cent, $\frac{5}{100}$ of it is taken off.

Look up **percentages** if you need to know more about this.

Reduce to its lowest terms means bring down to the lowest numbers you can.

$\frac{5}{10}$ reduced to its lowest terms $= \frac{1}{2}$

$\frac{8}{4} = 2$

reflex angles

These are angles which are between 180° and 360°. If you want to know more, look up **angles**.

Reflex angles are so wide open they look as if they have been bent backwards.

regular shapes

If a shape has all its sides and all its angles equal, it is called a regular shape or a regular figure. The sections on **polygons** or **polyhedron** might interest you.

relations

Relations are ***connections***. Family relations are connected to each other by birth or marriage.
Relations in Maths are connections too.

A **mapping** is a kind of relation.
There can be a relation between **sets** and between members of one set and another.
Ordered pairs can be relations.
A **ratio** is a kind of relation.

remainders

Left-overs.　　$6 \div 2 = 3$

$7 \div 2 = 3$ remainder 1
(We can write 3 rem 1 or 3 r 1)

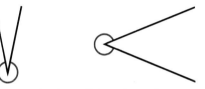

revolution

A revolution is a complete turn. A bicycle wheel makes one revolution every time it goes round.

rhombus

A rhombus is a quadrilateral. That means it is a four-sided shape. The sides are all equal in length. The opposite sides are parallel. It looks like a square which has had a push!

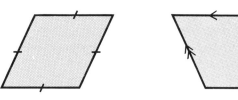

right angles

Angles of 90° are called right angles. (They are often marked on diagrams by a tiny square.) Set squares are useful for drawing right angles.

To make a useful right angle, fold any scrap of paper into four like this:

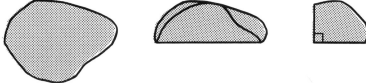

Make sure the edges of the folds are level.
You now have a right angle which is useful for checking the size of any other angle. Look up **angles** if you want more information about them.

right-angled triangle

A triangle which has one angle of 90°. (90° is a right angle.)

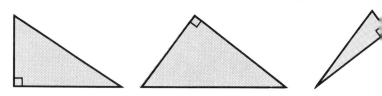

The right angle is often marked with a tiny square on diagrams. Look up the section on **triangles** if you want more information about them.

Roman numerals

I	II	III	IV	V	VI	VII	VIII	IX	X
1	2	3	4	5	6	7	8	9	10

XI	XII	XIII	XIV	XV	XVI	XVII	XVIII	XIX	XX
11	12	13	14	15	16	17	18	19	20

XL	L	C	D	M
40	50	100	500	1000

Remember V = 5
IV is 1 before 5. IV = 4
VI is 1 after 5. VI = 6.

When Romans wrote down their numbers they put them in order with the largest first.
MD = 1500 (1000 and 500)
MDCL = 1650 (1000 + 500 + 100 + 50)
MDCLXVI = 1666 (1000 + 500 + 100 + 50 + 10 + 5 + 1)

The only time you will see a smaller number **before** a larger number is when it has to be taken away.

L = 50
XL = 10 before 50. 10 less than 50.
XL = 40
CXL = 140 (100 and 10–before–50)
CLX = 160 (100 and 50 and 10)
MCM = 1900 (1000 and 100–before–1000) = 1000 and 900
MCMXCIX = 1999

rotate, rotation

A rotation is a turn. A complete rotation is a whole turn. It measures 360° (degrees).

rotational symmetry

Matching by turning.

Trace a shape on to two separate pieces of tracing paper. Put one exactly on top of the other and put a pin through the middle of the shapes. Turn the top shape carefully until it covers the bottom shape exactly again. If the two shapes match exactly before you have turned it all the way round we say they have rotational symmetry.

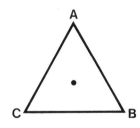

This shape is an equilateral triangle. Imagine it turning round.

1 It will match its own shape exactly when A is in B's place.

2 It will match again when A is in C's place.

3 It will match again when A is back at A's place.

This is called rotational symmetry of order 3. It matches its own shape 3 times in a complete turn.
The centre point (where the pin is) is called the centre of rotation.

round numbers

Round numbers usually end in a nought. Sometimes we don't need an exact answer to something: a rough idea is good enough. When we are using very large numbers round numbers are easier to deal with and easier to remember than exact numbers.
We may read in a newspaper that 15 000 people were at a special event. Nobody really believes that exactly 15 000 people were there. There might have been a few more. There might have been a few less. It doesn't really matter to us. The reporter used 'round numbers' to give us an idea of the size of the crowd.
Read the next section on **rounding off** too.

rounding off

By rounding off numbers we can find approximate answers. This is useful when we need a rough answer. It is also useful when we want to check our working out or a result we have got on a calculator. It shows us if we have got a sensible answer or if we are a long way out.

Rounding off to the nearest ten

When we round off to the nearest ten, we don't use any units. We round off the number to the nearest ten above it or below it whichever is nearer.
24 would be rounded off to 20.
27 would be rounded off to 30.
146 would be rounded off to 150.
1242 would be rounded off to 1240.
If you have a number ending in 5 it is halfway between two tens.
Round it up to the higher ten.
45 would be rounded up to 50.

Rounding off to the nearest hundred

When we round off to the nearest hundred, we don't use any tens or units. We round off the number to the hundred above it or below it, whichever is the nearer.
140 would be rounded off to 100.
162 would be rounded off to 200.
232 would be rounded off to 200.
1483 would be rounded off to 1500.
1449 would be rounded off to 1400.
If you have a number ending exactly in 50 it is halfway between two hundreds. Round it up to the hundred above it.
1250 would be rounded off to 1300.

Rounding off to the nearest thousand

When we round off to the nearest thousand, we don't use any hundreds, tens or units. We round off the number to the nearest thousand above or below it, whichever is nearer.
1427 would be rounded off to 1000.
1538 would be rounded off to 2000.
15960 would be rounded off to 16000.
19247 would be rounded off to 19000.
If you have a number ending exactly in 500 it is halfway between two thousands. Round it up to the thousand above it.
14500 would be rounded off to 15000.

Using the same idea we can 'round off' to the nearest pound, kilometre, litre, kilogram and so on.

We can also 'round off' to the nearest whole number if we are dealing with fractions or decimals.
With decimals we can 'round off' to a certain number of decimal places.

$\simeq$ and $\approx$ are both signs which are used to stand for approximately equal to.

SI units

SI is short for **Système International d'Unités**, the International System of Units. It is difficult to trade with other countries, to compare scientific results and so on, if people are measuring in different units.

SI units are now used by many countries.

The three kinds you may need to know about now are:

The SI unit of length which is the metre (m).

The SI unit of mass which is the kilogram (kg).

The SI unit of time which is the second (s).

These are called the SI base units. All the other units of length, mass and time can be worked out from these. If you want to know more, look up **metric system** or **time**.

scale

A model may be built 'to scale'. You may have a kit for making a scale model of a plane or a famous building. Set designers make scale models of the sets they will use for television programmes or stage plays. If a model is built to scale every part of it is carefully measured and made smaller in the same way.

A diagram or a map or plan may be drawn to scale. Usually a plan can't be drawn life-size. It has to fit on to a piece of paper. Everything that is to show on the plan is carefully measured and made smaller in the same way.

— 70 cm —

1 cm represent 20 cm
The scale is 1:20

← 70 cm →

1 cm represents 35 cm
The scale is 1:35

If something which is 1 metre long is drawn as 1 centimetre long, we say 1 cm represents 1 m. On that scale something which measures 2 metres in real life would be drawn 2 centimetres long. Something measuring $\frac{1}{2}$ metre in real life would measure $\frac{1}{2}$ centimetre on the plan.

A scale of 1:20 (we say 1 to 20) means that each measurement is $\frac{1}{20}$ of the real life measurement.

1 cm would stand for 20 cm.

2 cm would stand for 40 cm.

The real-life measurements would be 20 × the measurements on the plan or model.

A scale of 1:100 (1 to 100) would mean that
1 cm would stand for 100 cm (1 metre).

Every measurement would be $\frac{1}{100}$ of the real-life measurement.

The real-life measurements would be 100 × the measurements on the plan or model.

If you are comparing different models or plans remember to look at the scales. If the scales are different it is very difficult to compare them. You may need to work out or estimate the real-life sizes.

There may be more information to interest you in the sections on **plans** or **ratio**

scalene triangle

A triangle which has no equal sides. There is a section on **triangles** if you want to know more about them.

score

1 A score can be a number of points you have won in a game.

2 It is also an old-fashioned name for twenty. 3 score years and ten means 70 years (3 twenties plus ten).

3 If you are making a model out of cardboard you may be told to score the folds. This means that you rule a line with something sharp instead of a pencil wherever you need to make a fold. Your thumbnail may be sharp enough – it depends how thick the cardboard is. Scoring the lines makes it much easier to make a crisp fold. Make sure you don't cut right through though!

second

A measure of time.

60 seconds = 1 minute

60 minutes = 1 hour

30 seconds = $\frac{1}{2}$ minute

15 seconds = $\frac{1}{4}$ minute

45 seconds = $\frac{3}{4}$ minute.

There is more information in the section on **time**.

sector

A sector of a circle is like a slice of pie.

The sides of the slice are radii of the circle.

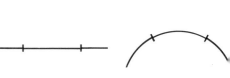

segment

A segment is part of something. A line segment is part of a longer line.

A segment of a circle

A segment of a circle is part of a circle which has been cut off by a chord.
When a straight line divides a circle into two parts, the larger part is called the major segment and the smaller part is called the minor segment.

If the two segments are equal they are *semi-circles* and the straight line is a *diameter*.

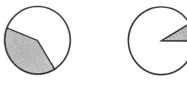

minor segment

major segment

semi-circle

A semi-circle is half a circle.

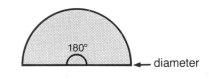

180°

← diameter

sequence

We talk about a dance sequence, a number sequence, a sequence of events.

In a sequence things follow on one after another with no gaps in the arrangements.

The sequence of *prime numbers* is 2, 3, 5, 7, 11, 13 …
The sequence of *square numbers* is 1, 4, 9, 16, 25 …
The sequence of *triangular numbers* is 1, 3, 6, 10, 15 …
The sequence of *rectangular numbers* is 4, 6, 8, 9, 10, 12 …

Read **series** – the next section – as well.

series

We talk about a series of television programmes, a series of magazines, a series of numbers.

A series of things is linked together in some way.

A series can be a sequence of things following on one after another. (Read about **sequence** just above this section.)

Sometimes we need to write down the next numbers in a series.

6   10   14   18   –   –

Look at the numbers. If you can see a pattern in them you can carry on with the pattern to find the next numbers.

If you can't see a pattern see if the numbers are getting bigger or smaller. See how you can get from one number to the next.

6^{+4} 10^{+4} 14^{+4} 18^{+4} $\underline{22}^{+4}$ $\underline{26}$

Here four was added on to the first number to bring it up to 10. Four was added on to the 10 to bring it up to 14 and so on.

If the numbers are getting bigger something may be added on to them or they may be multiplied by something.

If numbers are getting smaller, something may be subtracted (taken away) from them or they may be divided by something.

5   6   8   11   –   –

Here 1 is added to 5 to make 6
     2 is added to 6 to make 8
     3 is added to 8 to make 11.

To carry on the pattern we add 4 to the 11, making 15. Next we add 5 to 15 making 20.

5^{+1} 6^{+2} 8^{+3} 11^{+4} $\underline{15}^{+5}$ $\underline{20}$

20   17   14   11   –   –

$(20^{-3}$ 17^{-3} 14^{-3} 11^{-3} $\underline{8}^{-3}$ $\underline{5})$

Here 3 is taken away from each number to get to the next.

set square

A set square is a triangle made out of wood or plastic. One of its angles is a right angle. It would fit the corner of a square.

Sometimes the other two angles on a set square are equal and measure 45° each. Sometimes the other angles measure 60° and 30°.

A set square is useful for measuring and drawing right angles. It can be used for drawing *perpendicular* lines. By sliding the bottom edge of a set square along a straight line we can rule *parallel* lines. Experiment and see.

sets

We are used to talking about train sets, tea sets, chess sets and chemistry sets. We can have sets of all sorts of things. Each set is a collection of things which belong together. In Maths, collections of things which belong together are called sets. The things which belong to a set are called **members** of the set or **elements**.

Here is a set of fruit: {apples, pears, plums, cherries}.
Apples, pears, plums and cherries are members of the set.

Curly brackets are drawn round the members of a set. { }
Curly brackets are sometimes called **braces**.
Commas are always used to separate the members from each other.

To save time a **capital letter** can be used to stand for the name of the set. We must always say what the capital letter stands for though.

The set of vegetables in my store = {potatoes, carrots, onions}.
V = vegetables in my store.
V = {potatoes, carrots, onions}.

∈ is a symbol which means 'is a member of' (or 'are members of')
∉ is a symbol which means 'is not a member of'

Hammer ∈ {tools} means
Hammer is a member of the set of tools.

3 ∈ {odd numbers} means
3 is a member of the set of odd numbers.

4 ∉ {odd numbers} means
4 is not a member of the set of odd numbers.

Empty sets

An empty set is a set with no members. { } stands for an empty set. There is nothing between the brackets.
∅ stands for an empty set as well.
Sometimes an empty set is called a **null set**.

Equal sets

Sets are equal if they have exactly the same members.

Identical sets

Identical sets are equal.
= means equals
≠ means is not equal to.

If M = {5p, 10p, 20p, 50p} and
C = {50p, 10p, 20p, 5p}
$M = C$

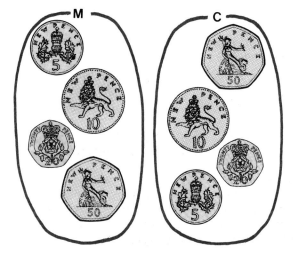

The members of each set are exactly the same although they haven't been written down in the same order.

Sometimes a ring is drawn round members of a set. These 'ring pictures' are called **Venn diagrams**.

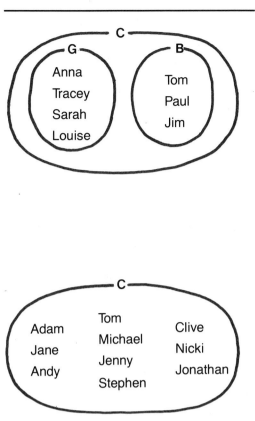

Subsets

Sometimes a set is divided up into smaller sets. The smaller sets are called subsets of the main set.

C = a set of children

C = {Anna, Tracey, Sarah, Tom, Paul, Louise, Jim}

This set could be divided into a subset of girls (G) and a subset of boys (B)

G = {Anna, Tracey, Sarah, Louise}

B = {Tom, Paul, Jim}

$\subset$ means 'is a subset of'

$G \subset C$ means G is a subset of C.

$B \subset C$ means B is a subset of C

$\not\subset$ means 'is not a subset of'

C = {children in Adam's road}

B = {children who play in the band}

S = {children who sing in the choir}

$B \subset C$ (B is a subset of C)

$S \subset C$ (S is a subset of C)

S and B have not got the same members, so $S \neq B$.

Intersection

Tom and Adam play in the band and they sing in the choir. They are in both subsets.

S = {Jenny, Nicki, Jonathan, Tom, Adam}

B = {Jane, Andy, Michael, Tom, Adam}

When two sets overlap each other like this we say they intersect. The overlap is an intersection.

The sign for intersection is $\cap$

$S \cap B$ = {Tom, Adam}

sharing

When we talk about sharing we usually mean sharing equally.

$\div$ is the sign for sharing or dividing.

Share 10 sweets between 2 children.

They would have 5 sweets each.

$10 \div 2 = 5$.

To share things we divide them up into equal groups.

If you want to know more about this kind of equal sharing look up **division**.

If you want to know about sharing when one person has a certain amount more than another – or something costs a certain amount more than another, look up **unequal sharing**. If you need to know what to do when one amount is a number of times more than another amount, look up **proportion**.

signs and symbols

+	add, plus, positive	°	degrees
−	subtract, take away, minus, negative	°C	degrees Celsius
		°F	degrees Fahrenheit
×	multiply	≃	approximately equal to
÷	divide	≈	approximately equal to
<	less than	%	per cent
>	more than	π	pi

(Imagine this is a hungry mouth <. It opens towards the bigger amount always. 3<10, 10>3.)

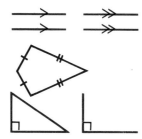

little arrowheads on lines tell us that they are parallel lines.

little dashes on lines tell us that they are equal in length.

a little square in an angle tells us that it is a right angle (90°).

∠	angle	△	triangle	□	square
∥	parallel to	⊥	perpendicular to	√	the square root of

Signs and symbols to do with sets

{ }	Curly brackets like this are put round the members of a set.
{ }	an empty set. There is nothing between the brackets. The set has no members.
∅	an empty set. This symbol is also used when a set has no members.
=	equals
≠	is not equal to
∈	is a member of
∉	is not a member of
⊂	is a subset of
⊄	is not a subset of
∩	intersection (A∩B means that some members of set A are also members of set B.)

If you want to know the symbols for different measurements, look up **SI units** and **Imperial units**.

simplify

If we simplify something we make it as easy to deal with as possible.

To simplify a fraction we bring it down to its lowest terms.

$$\frac{\cancel{10}^2}{\cancel{15}_3} = \frac{2}{3}$$

(Look up **fractions** if you have forgotten about this.)

To simplify an expression, a maths sentence or an equation, we work it out and put the answer as simply as we can.

$4 + 10 - 8 = 14 - 8 = \underline{6}$

$n + \ \ 6 = 10$

$4 + \ \ 6 = 10$

$\underline{n = 4}$

If you want to know more, look up **equations**.

solid figures
solids

Solid figures are shapes which take up space in all directions. They are not flat 'plane' shapes like squares and circles.
A solid figure which is round in every direction is called a **sphere**.
Here are some more solid figures:

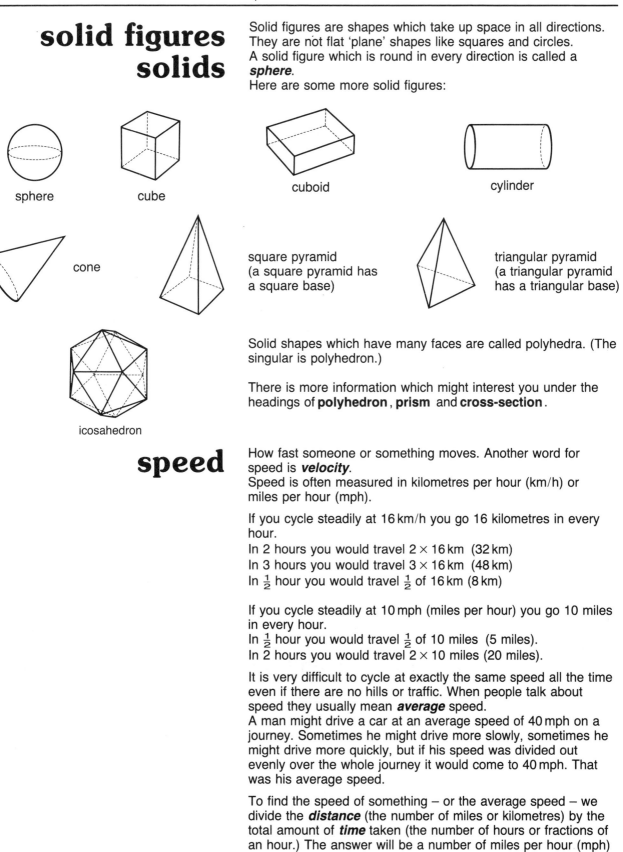

sphere   cube   cuboid   cylinder

cone

square pyramid
(a square pyramid has
a square base)

triangular pyramid
(a triangular pyramid
has a triangular base)

icosahedron

Solid shapes which have many faces are called polyhedra. (The singular is polyhedron.)

There is more information which might interest you under the headings of **polyhedron**, **prism** and **cross-section**.

speed

How fast someone or something moves. Another word for speed is **velocity**.
Speed is often measured in kilometres per hour (km/h) or miles per hour (mph).

If you cycle steadily at 16 km/h you go 16 kilometres in every hour.
In 2 hours you would travel 2×16 km (32 km)
In 3 hours you would travel 3×16 km (48 km)
In $\frac{1}{2}$ hour you would travel $\frac{1}{2}$ of 16 km (8 km)

If you cycle steadily at 10 mph (miles per hour) you go 10 miles in every hour.
In $\frac{1}{2}$ hour you would travel $\frac{1}{2}$ of 10 miles (5 miles).
In 2 hours you would travel 2×10 miles (20 miles).

It is very difficult to cycle at exactly the same speed all the time even if there are no hills or traffic. When people talk about speed they usually mean **average** speed.
A man might drive a car at an average speed of 40 mph on a journey. Sometimes he might drive more slowly, sometimes he might drive more quickly, but if his speed was divided out evenly over the whole journey it would come to 40 mph. That was his average speed.

To find the speed of something – or the average speed – we divide the **distance** (the number of miles or kilometres) by the total amount of **time** taken (the number of hours or fractions of an hour.) The answer will be a number of miles per hour (mph) or kilometres per hour (km/h).

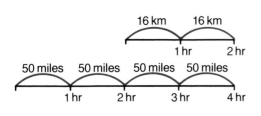

Speed (in mph) = distance (in miles) ÷ time (in hours)
Speed (in km/h) = distance (in km) ÷ time (in hours)

If a girl cycles for 32 km and takes 2 hours to do it her average speed is 16 km/h (32 ÷ 2 = 16).

If a man drives for 200 miles and takes 4 hours to do it, his average speed is 50 mph (200 ÷ 4 = 50).

You might find it helpful to look up the sections on **distance** and **time**.

sphere

A sphere is a solid shape which is round in every direction like a ball.

square

1 A square has four sides which are all the same length. Each angle is a right angle (90°).

2 To square a number we multiply it by itself.

4 squared is written as 4^2.
It means 4×4. $4^2 = 16$.

6 squared is written as 6^2.
It means 6×6. $6^2 = 36$.

10 squared is written as 10^2.
It means 10×10. $10^2 = 100$.

1 squared is written as 1^2.
It means 1×1. $1^2 = 1$.

square numbers

When a number is multiplied by itself the answer is a square number.

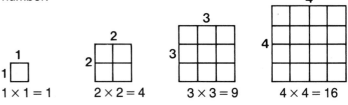

$1 \times 1 = 1$ $2 \times 2 = 4$ $3 \times 3 = 9$ $4 \times 4 = 16$

1, 4, 9, 16 are all square numbers.

The next square numbers are:
25 (5×5) 36 (6×6) 49 (7×7)
64 (8×8) 81 (9×9) 100 (10×10) and so on.

square root

The square root sign is $\sqrt{}$ or $\sqrt{}$. $\sqrt{16}$ means the square root of 16.

$4 \times 4 = 16$ The square root of 16 is 4. $\sqrt{16} = 4$
$3 \times 3 = 9$ $\sqrt{9} = 3$
$5 \times 5 = 25$ $\sqrt{25} = 5$
$10 \times 10 = 100$ $\sqrt{100} = 10$

statistics
straight angles

Statistics are collections of facts and figures.

A straight angle is 180°. _____ 180°

Look up **angles** if you need to know more about them.

subsets

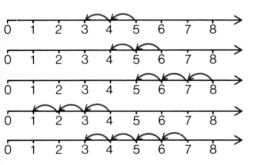

A set which is part of another set is called a subset. The symbol for subset is ⊂.
N is a set of whole numbers up to 10.
E is a subset of N. It is a set of even numbers up to 10.

$N = \{1, 2, 3, 4, 5, 6, 7, 8, 9, 10\}$
$E = \{2, 4, 6, 8, 10\}$
$E \subset N$ (E is a subset of N)
Look up **sets** if you want to know more about sets and subsets.

subtraction

Subtraction is 'taking away'. The answer is the number which is left.

Here are four sweets.

If we subtract 1, we take away 1.
3 are left.

The sign we use for subtraction is −. It is called the minus sign.
$4 - 1 = 3$.

We can use subtraction for all the following examples.

From 5 **take away** 2	O O O Ø Ø	$5 - 2 = 3$
From 6 **subtract** 2	O O O O Ø Ø	$6 - 2 = 4$
8 **minus** 3	O O O O O Ø Ø Ø	$8 - 3 = 5$
Decrease 4 by 3	O Ø Ø Ø	$4 - 3 = 1$
Reduce 7 by 4	O O O Ø Ø Ø Ø	$7 - 4 = 3$
How many more is 6 than 5?	O O O O O O	$6 - 5 = 1$
By how many is 4 **more** than 1?	O O O O	$4 - 1 = 3$
How many fewer than 5 is 3?	O O O O O	$5 - 3 = 2$

Think what you are doing if you have examples like the next ones. Don't just write down the first number you come to.
Take 6 from 10.
You must write down 10 first so that you can take 6 away from it.

Take 6 from 10 means	$10 - 6$.	$10 - 6 = 4$
Subtract 4 from 5 means	$5 - 4$.	$5 - 4 = 1$
Deduct 5 from 7 means	$7 - 5$.	$7 - 5 = 2$

4 less than 6	$6 - 4 = 2$
By how much is 6 less than 8?	$8 - 6 = 2$
Which number is 4 less than 7?	$7 - 4 = 3$
How many is 4 less than 5?	$5 - 4 = 1$

When we find the difference between two amounts we have to compare them.
What is the difference between 6 and 4?

6 is 2 more than 4. The difference between 6 and 4 is 2.
$6 - 4 = 2$
(There is more about this under **difference** if you need it.)

supplementary angles

A pair of angles which make up 180° when they are added together.

symbols

Signs we use to stand for words. They save time and trouble as long as everyone knows what they stand for.
There is a list of useful ones under **signs**.

symmetrical

With both halves matching.

Read the next section on **symmetry**.

symmetry

The diagrams in the section just above all show symmetry. It is possible to divide each of them into two matching halves. The dividing line is called the line of symmetry or the axis of symmetry. Some shapes have more than one line of symmetry.

The letter H could be divided like this  or like this

Both halves would match either way.
It has two lines (or **axes**) of symmetry.

A square has four lines (or axes) of symmetry.

If a symmetrical shape is cut out and folded along the line of symmetry, one side will fit exactly on top of the other.

tables

When information about something is written down in a list it is often called a table. We talk about a table of results in science, tables of measurements, multiplication tables, timetables and so on.

A multiplication table is a list of equal groups already counted up. Read the section on **multiplication** if you want to know how they are built up and what they mean.

It really is worthwhile learning the multiplication tables. Once you know them you can save yourself lots of time and trouble for the rest of your life.

Here are some useful tables of measurements.

Metric units

Length (linear measurements)
10 millimetres (mm) = 1 centimetre (cm)
100 centimetres   = 1 metre (m)
1000 metres   = 1 kilometre (km)

Area
100 square millimetres (mm^2) = 1 square centimetre (cm^2)
10000 square centimetres   = 1 square metre (m^2)
10000 square metres   = 1 hectare (ha)

Mass (or weight)
1000 grams (g)   = 1 kilogram (kg)
1000 kilograms   = 1 tonne

You might need:
1000 milligrams (mg) = 1 gram
100 grams   = 1 hectogram
10 hectograms   = 1 kilogram (kg)

Capacity
1000 millilitres (ml) = 1 litre (l)

Imperial units

These used to be the standard measurements in Britain. Some of them are still used. These are the ones you are most likely to meet:

Length
12 inches (in) = 1 foot (ft)
3 feet (ft)   = 1 yard (yd)
1760 yd   = 1 mile

Area
144 square inches = 1 sq ft
9 square feet   = 1 sq yd
4840 sq yd   = 1 acre

Mass (or weight)
16 ounces (oz) = 1 pound (lb)
14 lb   = 1 stone (st)
112 lb   = 1 hundredweight (cwt)
20 cwt   = 1 ton

Capacity
8 pints (pt) = 1 gallon (gal)

If you want to know how to change from one unit of measurement to another (centimetres to metres, pounds to grams and so on) look up   .

tally
tallying

Tallying was an early way of counting. It didn't need number names or figures. A man could check the number of animals he had by putting down a stone or a stick as each one went past him. Another way of tallying was to cut a notch in a stick as each one went past. The number of animals would match the number of stones or sticks or notches. The numbers would tally.

Later tally sticks were used for keeping accounts. A piece of wood would be marked across with notches to show the items on an account. Then it would be split down the middle so that each person could have a matching stick.

There are times when tallying is useful nowadays. It can be especially useful when we are counting things which are moving – like the vehicles passing the school gate or deliveries from a lorry. When we tally now we use straight lines instead of numbers or sticks for counting.

We do it like this: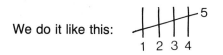

We don't write the numbers down (1 2 3 4 5) we just do the 'sticks'.

It is easy to count up all the fives afterwards. This would represent 17:

tangent

This means touching. A tangent is a straight line which 'just touches'.

Here is a tangent to a circle.

It is a straight line outside the circle which just touches the circumference in one place.

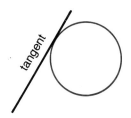

tessellate
tessellations

If shapes tessellate they fit together without any gaps.

These are examples of tessellations. They are made from tessellating shapes.

These shapes will not tessellate.

However they are arranged, gaps are left in between them.

tetrahedron

A tetrahedron is a four-sided solid.
A regular tetrahedron has an
equilateral triangle for each face.

Look up **polyhedron** if you want more
information about solid shapes.

time

60 seconds (s) = 1 minute
60 minutes   = 1 hour
24 hours   = 1 day
half an hour ($\frac{1}{2}$ hr) = 30 minutes
a quarter of an hour ($\frac{1}{4}$ hr) = 15 minutes
three quarters of an hour ($\frac{3}{4}$ hr) = 45 minutes
7 days   = 1 week
(14 days together = 1 fortnight)
52 weeks = 1 year
12 months = 1 year
365 days = 1 year
366 days = 1 leap year

Look up **leap year** if you need to know about it.
Roman numerals seen on some clocks

I = 1	VII = 7
II = 2	VIII = 8
III = 3	IX = 9
IIII or IV = 4	X = 10
V = 5	XI = 11
VI = 6	XII = 12

Telling the time

There are many different kinds of clocks and watches.

Usually they show us the time on a face

like this

or this.

Look at the first clock face.

The hands go round this way.
(We call this clockwise.)

The little hand is the hour hand. The big hand is the minute
hand.

The hour hand tells us what hour it is.

At 1 o'clock it points to 1.
At 2 o'clock it points to 2.
At 3 o'clock it points to 3.

It takes the little hand a whole hour to move from one number to the next. In 12 hours the little hand goes all the way round the clock face once.

The big hand goes much faster. It moves from one number to the next in five minutes. It goes all the way round the clock face in one hour. In 12 hours the big hand goes round 12 times.

This shows
1 o'clock.
We can write 1.00.

This shows
2 o'clock.
We can write 2.00.

This shows
3 o'clock.
We can write 3.00.

In a quarter of an hour the minute hand goes a quarter of the way round the clock. A quarter of an hour is 15 minutes.

In a quarter of an hour the hour hand moves a quarter of the way towards the next number.

This shows
quarter past 1
We can write 1.15.

This shows
quarter past 2
We can write 2.15.

This shows
quarter past 3.
We can write 3.15.

In half an hour the minute hand goes half-way round the clock. Half an hour is 30 minutes. In half an hour the hour hand goes half-way from one number to the next.

This shows
half past 1.
We can write 1.30.

This shows
half past 2.
We can write 2.30.

This shows
half past 3.
We can write 3.30.

These clock faces show some of the 'in between' times.

This shows
10 o'clock.
We can write 10.00.

This shows
5 minutes past 10.
We can write 10.05.

This shows
0 minutes past 10.
We can write 10.10.

This shows
15 minutes past 10.
It is a quarter of an
hour past 10
o'clock. We can call
it quarter past 10 or
10.15. We usually
write 10.15.

This shows
20 minutes past 10.
We can write 10.20.

This shows
25 minutes past 10.
We can write 10.25.

This shows
30 minutes past 10.
It is half an hour
past 10 o'clock. We
can call it half past
10 or 10.30.
We usually write
10.30.

When the minute hand has gone more than half-way round the
clock face it starts coming up towards the next hour. We can
say it is so many minutes **past** the hour or it is so many
minutes **to** the next hour.

This shows
35 minutes past 10.
We write 10.35.
We can also call it
35 to 11. It is 25
minutes before 11
o'clock.

This shows
40 minutes past 10.
We write 10.40.
We can also call it
20 to 11. It is 20
minutes before 11
o'clock.

This shows
45 minutes past 10.
We write 10.45.
We can also call it
quarter to 11. It is a
quarter of an hour
(15 minutes) before
11 o'clock.

This shows
50 minutes past 10.
We write 10.50.
We can also call it
10 to 11. It is ten
minutes before 11
o'clock.

This shows
55 minutes past 10.
We write 10.55.
We can also call it 5
to 11. It is five
minutes before 11
o'clock.

Digital clocks and watches don't have hands. They show us the
time just as we would write it down.

Midday and midnight

Midday is at 12 o'clock in the middle of the day.
It is also called 12 noon.
Midnight is 12 o'clock at night.

a.m. and p.m.

a.m. stands for *ante meridiem*.
It is Latin for before midday.
p.m. stands for *post meridiem*.
It is Latin for after midday.
5 a.m. means 5 o'clock in the morning.
5 p.m. means 5 o'clock in the afternoon.

Any time after midnight and before midday is a.m.
Any time after midday and up to midnight is p.m.

There is a separate section on the **twenty-four hour clock**.
Look it up if you need to know about it.

Fast and slow, gaining and losing

We say a clock or a watch is gaining if it is working too
quickly. If it showed the time as 9.30 when it was only 9.25 we
would say it was 5 minutes fast. It was 5 minutes ahead of the
real time.

If we were told that a clock was 20 minutes fast we would
know that it was 20 minutes ahead of the real time. We would
have to count back 20 minutes to find out the real time. If it
showed the time as 8.40 the real time would be 8.20.

Sometimes we are told that a clock is gaining – say – five
minutes an hour. That means that it is gaining 5 minutes **every**
hour.
Suppose it showed the right time at 2 o'clock. At 3 o'clock it
would show the time as 3.05. One hour later it would have
gained another 5 minutes.
At 4 o'clock it would show the time as 4.10. One hour later it
would have gained another 5 minutes.
It would carry on gaining 5 minutes every hour until it was put
right.
In 10 hours it would be $10 \times 5 = 50$ minutes fast.
In 12 hours it would be $12 \times 5 = 60$ minutes fast.

We say a clock or a watch is losing time if it is working too
slowly. If it showed the time as 6.15 when it was really 6.20 we
would say it was 5 minutes slow. It was 5 minutes behind the
real time.

If we were told that a clock was 20 minutes slow we would
know that it was 20 minutes behind the real time. We would
have to count *on* 20 minutes to find out the real time. If it
showed the time as 6.05 the real time would be 6.25.

Sometimes we are told that a clock is losing – say – five
minutes an hour. This means that it is losing 5 minutes **every**
hour.

Suppose it showed the right time at 2 o'clock.
At 3 o'clock it would show the time as 2.55.
An hour later it would have lost another 5 minutes.
At 4 o'clock it would show the time not as 3.55 but 3.50.
An hour later it would have lost another 5 minutes.

It would carry on losing 5 minutes every hour until it was put right.
In 10 hours it would be 50 minutes slow (10 × 5 minutes)
In 12 hours it would be 60 minutes slow (12 × 5 minutes)

How long does it take?

We often need to know how long it is from one time to another. How long does a television programme last? How long has a cake been in the oven? How long does a journey last?
Here are some examples.

1 A programme starts at 5.10 p.m. It ends at 5.35 p.m. How long does it last?
We could count on from 5.10 to 5.35.

5.10 to 5.20 = 10 mins
5.20 to 5.30 = 10 mins
5.30 to 5.35 = 5 mins
The whole time
5.10 to 5.35 = 25 mins

The programme lasts for 25 minutes.

2 A cake was put in the oven at 11.15 a.m. It is now 12.20 p.m. How long has it been in the oven?

We could count on from 11.15 to 12.20
11.15 to 12.00 (midday) = 45 minutes
12.00 to 12.20   = 20 minutes
Altogether 11.15 to 12.20 = 65 minutes

The cake has been in the oven for 65 minutes. 60 minutes = 1 hour. We could say the cake has been in the oven for 1 hour 5 minutes.

3 A journey starts at 10.06 a.m. and finishes at 2.30 p.m. How long does it take?
We could count on from 10.06 a.m. to 2.30 p.m.
10.06 to 11.06 = 1 hour
11.06 to 12.06 = 1 hour
12.06 to 1.06 = 1 hour
 1.06 to 2.06 = 1 hour
 2.06 to 2.30 = 24 minutes

Altogether the journey takes 4 hours 24 minutes

Time, distance and speed

Speed is often measured in kilometres per hour (km/h) or in metres per second. The old measures of miles per hour (mph) are also still used.
If a cyclist travelled at 30 km/h, he would travel 30 kilometres in every hour.
60 kilometres would take 2 hours.
90 kilometres would take 3 hours.
15 kilometres would take $\frac{1}{2}$ hour (15 = $\frac{1}{2}$ of 30).

If a car travelled at an average speed of 40 mph (miles per hour), how long would it take for a journey of 100 miles?

40 miles would take 1 hour
Another 40 miles would take another hour
80 miles would take 2 hours
20 miles would take $\frac{1}{2}$ hour
100 miles (80 + 20) would take $2\frac{1}{2}$ hours
You might find it helpful to look up **speed** and **distance**.

Short amounts of time are measured in seconds. Sometimes a second hand on a watch is good enough for this. Sometimes a stop watch is better. It can be started and stopped quickly and its face is clearly marked in seconds and fractions of a second.

When we think about time we usually think about clocks and watches. Time is not just the passing of hours, minutes and seconds. It can be about the passing of days, weeks, months, years and centuries.

There are several sections in this book which might be useful to you:
AD, BC, calendar, century, dates, leap year, timetables, twenty-four hour clock. The sections on **distance** and **speed** might be helpful too.

times

This means multiplied by. The sign is ×. When people say 'times' they often mean multiplication.

To find 5 times 2 we multiply.

5 times 2 means 5×2

5 times 2 = 10

If Tracey has £4 and Sarah has three times as much, Sarah has $3 \times £4$.

Sarah has £12.

Instead of two times we often say *twice*.

If you have forgotten about **multiplication** look it up.

timetables

Timetables are lists of times which are used to tell us when something happens. School timetables show the times when different lessons start and stop.

Most timetables are to do with travelling and most of them use the twenty-four-hour clock.

24-hour clock times are written using four figures. The first two are hours. The last two are minutes. After 12.00 midday, the hours carry on 13.00, 14.00, 15.00 and so on to 24.00 which is midnight.

This means that 1 a.m. is written as 01.00 and 1 p.m. is written as 13.00. It is not so easy to muddle up a morning time with an afternoon time. If you have forgotten about this look up the section on the **twenty-four hour clock**.

Here is part of a train timetable.

Castleton depart	Dunsford arrive
10.35	12.40
13.20	15.35
17.35	19.40

This shows the times that trains leave Castleton and the time they arrive at Dunsford. We can work out how long each train takes if we need to.

1 We can count on from the time it leaves Castleton to the time it arrives at Dunsford.

	hours	minutes
10.35 to 11.35 =	1 hour	
11.35 to 12.35 =	1 hour	
12.35 to 12.40 =		5 minutes

Altogether 10.35 to 12.40 = 2 hours 5 minutes

The first train takes 2 hours 5 minutes.

2 To find the number of hours and minutes between 10.35 and 12.40 we could subtract.

	hours	minutes
	12	40
−	10	35
	2 hours	5 minutes

The first train takes 2 hours 5 minutes.

This timetable is arranged differently.

Whiteway depart	10.25	11.25	12.25
Wolford	11.45	12.45	—
Barringdon arrive	13.15	14.15	15.00

The first train leaves Whiteway at 10.25.
It stops at Wolford at 11.45.
It arrives at Barringdon at 13.15 (1.15 p.m.).

The second train leaves Whiteway at 11.25.
It stops at Wolford at 12.45.
It arrives at Barringdon at 14.15 (2.15 p.m.).

The third train leaves Whiteway at 12.25.
It does not stop at Wolford.
It arrives at Barringdon at 15.00 (3.00 p.m.).

Remember the fastest train – or bus – takes the shortest time. It gets along more quickly than the others.

The slowest train – or bus – takes the longest time.

ton

An Imperial measure of mass or weight. (Look up **mass** if you are not sure about this.)
1 ton = 20 hundredweight (cwt)
1 ton = 2240 pounds (lb)
People used to buy coal by the hundredweight (cwt) or the ton.

tonne

A tonne is a metric measure of mass or weight. (Look up **mass** if you are not sure about this.)
1 tonne (t) = 1000 kilograms (kg).

topological transformation

'Topo' comes from the Greek work topos. It means a place or a spot. A transformation is a change.

You make a topological transformation every time you roll out a piece of pastry, squash a piece of plasticine, stretch a piece of elastic or chew bubble gum.

The rules are that you may examine your shape on all sides, bend it, twist it, stretch it, roll it up, flatten it, but ***not*** tear it or break it or join it up differently.

topology

Any word ending *'logy'* means a study of something.
'Topo' comes from the Greek work topos. It means a place or a spot.

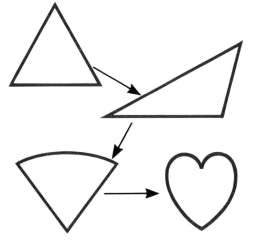

When you study a triangle you look at the lengths of its three sides, the sizes of its three angles and sometimes its area.
It is a fixed shape and that's that. In topology you have much more freedom. You study all sides of a shape, inside as well as outside. You can study all the space around it as well as in it. That is not all! You can imagine it stretched or twisted. You can pull out the points of your shape – or push them in.

You can also imagine your shape pumped up! You don't have to start off with a flat shape. You can have a solid lump of any size or shape. You can start off with points and lines and see how they are linked together. Topology can be a study of knots and networks.
Read the section on **topological transformations** just above this.

total

The total is the whole of something. The total cost is the whole cost.
To find the total we count up – or add up – the whole lot.
We add to find the total number
the total weight
the total amount
the total population
and so on.

trapezium

A trapezium is a four-sided shape (quadrilateral) with two parallel sides.

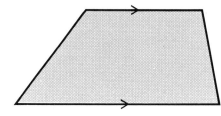
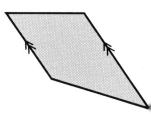

treble

Treble means multiply by three.

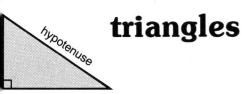

a right-angled triangle

triangles

A triangle is a flat shape with three straight sides and three angles.

The three angles of a triangle add up to 180°.

A right-angled triangle

This has an angle of 90° (90° is a right angle). The longest side is opposite this angle. It is called the **hypotenuse**.

An equilateral triangle

This has three equal angles and three sides of equal length.

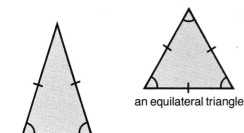

an equilateral triangle

an isosceles triangle

An isosceles triangle

This has two equal sides. The angles opposite these two sides are also equal.

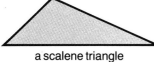

a scalene triangle

A scalene triangle

This has all the three sides of different lengths. The angles are all different too.

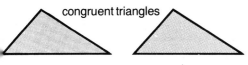

congruent triangles

Congruent triangles

Triangles which are exactly the same size and shape are called congruent.

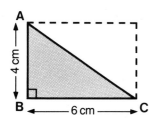

The area of a triangle

The area of a triangle is half the base × the height.

($\frac{1}{2} b \times h$ or $\frac{b \times h}{2}$ if you like.)

The area of triangle ABC is $\frac{1}{2}$ of 6 × 4 cm
= $\frac{1}{2}$ of 24 cm²
= 12 cm²

Remember that the height of a triangle is not necessarily the length of a side. Look at this one.

The height is shown.

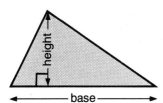

To find the height draw a line from the tip of the triangle to meet the base at right angles.

triangular numbers

A triangular number can be shown by a triangle of dots.

1 is counted as a triangular number. The next is 3, then 6, 10, 15, 21 and so on.

If you look at the sequence of triangular numbers you can see how it is built up.

1^{+2} 3^{+3} 6^{+4} 10^{+5} 15^{+6} 21 and so on.

If you look at the patterns of dots again you will see why.

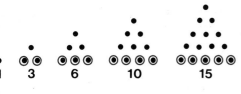

1   3   6   10   15

triangular prism

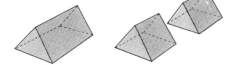

A prism is a special kind of solid shape. Its two ends are exactly the same size and shape and they are parallel to each other. The ends of a triangular prism are triangles. A triangular prism is shaped like a triangle all the way through its length.

If you slice through a triangular prism parallel to one of its ends, the new ends will be triangles too. The old ends and the new ends will match exactly.
You may use glass triangular prisms in science.

triangular pyramid

A pyramid which has a triangle for a base.

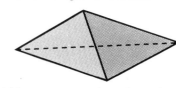

(A square pyramid has a square for a base.)

twenty-four hour clock

Most timetables use the 24-hour clock. Instead of counting the time up to 12.00 midday, then up to twelve again, the time is counted straight through from 0 to 24.

a.m.	24-hour clock times	p.m.	24-hour clock times
1 a.m.	= 01.00	1 p.m.	= 13.00
2 a.m.	= 02.00	2 p.m.	= 14.00
3 a.m.	= 03.00	3 p.m.	= 15.00
4 a.m.	= 04.00	4 p.m.	= 16.00
5 a.m.	= 05.00	5 p.m.	= 17.00
6 a.m.	= 06.00	6 p.m.	= 18.00
7 a.m.	= 07.00	7 p.m.	= 19.00
8 a.m.	= 08.00	8 p.m.	= 20.00
9 a.m.	= 09.00	9 p.m.	= 21.00
10 a.m.	= 10.00	10 p.m.	= 22.00
11 a.m.	= 11.00	11 p.m.	= 23.00
12 midday	= 12.00	12 midnight	= 24.00

It is not so easy to muddle up a morning time with an afternoon time if you use the 24-hour clock.

24-hour clock times are always written using four figures. The first two show the hour. The last two show the minutes.

00.01 would be 1 minute after midnight.
(The first minute of the new morning.)
00.30 would be 30 minutes after midnight.
01.30 would be 1.30 a.m.
10.45 would be 10.45 a.m.
13.30 would be 1.30 p.m.
15.27 would be 3.27 p.m.

The quick way to change times on the 24-hour clock to 'ordinary' times is to take 12 away from the hours. (You only need to do this for times between 13.00 and 24.00 of course.) The quick way to change p.m. times to 24-hour clock times is to add 12 to the hour.

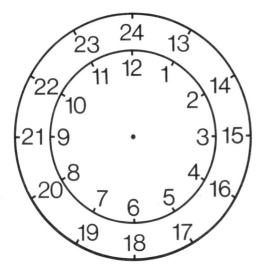

unequal sharing

When we talk about sharing things we usually mean sharing them equally or dividing them up into equal groups. Sometimes we need to share things out differently. Look at these examples.

Share 50p between Jan and Yvonne so that Jan has 10p more than Yvonne.

1 Give Jan her extra 10p.

2 Find out what is left.
50p − 10p = 40p

Jan	Yvonne
10p	

3 Share out what is left in the usual way.
40p ÷ 2 = 20p
They would each have 20p.

Jan	Yvonne
10p	
20p	20p
30p	20p

4 Jan has her 20p + the extra 10p.
Jan has 30p altogether.
Yvonne has 20p.

This uses up the 50p and Jan has 10p more than Yvonne.

A ruler and a pencil together cost £1. The ruler cost 50p more than the pencil. How much did they cost separately?

1 Put the extra 50p on one side for the ruler.
2 Find out how much is left.
£1 − 50p = 50p

Ruler	Pencil
50p	

3 Share out whatever is left in the usual way
50p ÷ 2 = 25p
Put out 25p each.
4 The ruler would cost
50p + 25p = 75p
The pencil would cost 25p.

Ruler	Pencil
50p	
25p	25p
75p	25p

That comes to £1 altogether – and the ruler does cost 50p more than the pencil.

Divide 7 apples between 2 boys so that one has 3 less than the other.

1 If one has 3 less, then give the other one 3 to start with.

Boy A	Boy B
	3

2 Find out how many are left.
7 − 3 = 4

3 Share out whatever is left in the usual way.
4 ÷ 2 = 2
They could have 2 each.

Boy A	Boy B
	3
2	2
2	5

4 One boy could have 2 apples. The other boy could have 5 apples.
(This uses up the 7 apples altogether and one boy does have 3 less than the other.)

There are other kinds of unequal sharing – where one person is paid three times as much as another for example. This kind is dealt with under **proportion** and **ratio**.

value

If you have to find the value of something, you have to find out what it is worth.

If two things are equal in value they are worth the same amount.

$$10 \times 5p = 50p \qquad \frac{2}{4} = \frac{1}{2}$$

When we multiply something by 1 its value does not change. It is still worth the same.

$$4 \times 1 = 4 \qquad £5 \times 1 = £5.$$

variable

If something is variable it is changeable. We talk about variable winds and variable weather. A variable in Maths is changeable too. It can change its value.

Sometimes a letter is used to stand for an amount in an equation. If it just stands for one amount which stays the same, it is called a **constant**. If it can stand for any one of a whole range of amounts it is called a **variable**.

velocity

This means speed. It is often measured in kilometres per hour (km/h) or metres per second (m/s). Sometimes it is measured in miles per hour (mph). Look up the section on **speed** if you want some examples of this.

Venn diagrams

These are sometimes called ring pictures. They are especially useful for sorting out **sets** and **subsets**.

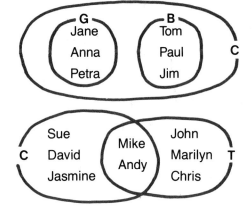

C is a set of children.

G is a subset of girls.

B is a subset of boys.

T is a set of people who drink tea.

C is a set of people who drink coffee.

Mike and Andy are in both circles.

They drink tea and coffee so the ovals overlap.

Look up **sets** if you want to know more about this.

vertex
vertices

The vertex is the top or tip. (The point furthest away from the base.) It can also be the corner point of a polygon or a polyhedron. The plural is vertices (say *verti-seez*).

X is the vertex of the cone.

A, B and C are the vertices of the triangle.

A pentagon has five vertices.

A cube has eight vertices.

vertical

vertical

horizontal

Vertical means exactly upright. A vertical line is at right angles to a horizontal line. This is also called perpendicular. A set square is useful for checking this.

A door must be fixed vertically into its door frame or it won't close properly. Wallpaper must be stuck on to walls vertically. A **plumb line** is useful for checking that something like this is exactly upright.

volume

This is the amount of space a shape takes up.

For example:
This cube is 1 cm long, 1 cm wide and 1 cm high.
We say its volume is 1 cubic centimetre.
We can write this as 1 cm^3.
It is the amount of space it takes up.

This cube is 3 cm long, 3 cm wide and 3 cm high.
It could be built up from 1 cm cubes.
Each layer would have 3 rows of cubes with 3 cubes in each row.

Each layer would need $3 \times 3 = 9$ cubes.

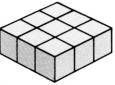

There would be 3 layers.
$3 \times 3 \times 3$ cubes would be needed altogether. $3 \times 3 \times 3 = 27$.
The volume of this cube would be 27 cm^3.

To find the volume of any cube or cuboid we multiply the length by the width (or breadth) by the height. We can write $l \times b \times h$ for short.

Remember All the measurements must be in the **same units** – they must all be cm or all mm and so on.

The answer is always in **cubic** measure. It could be m^3, cm^3 or mm^3.

$1000 \text{ mm}^3 = 1 \text{ cm}^3$

This cuboid is 10 cm long, 5 cm wide and 2 cm high.
$10 \times 5 \times 2 = 100$
Its volume is 100 cm^3.

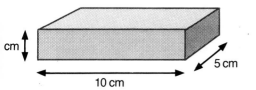

cm

5 cm

10 cm

The volume can be the amount a container can hold. This is sometimes called **capacity**.
We still multiply the length by the breadth by the height to find the number of **cubic units** a container can hold. The answer will still be cubic measure.

$1000 \text{ cm}^3 = 1 \text{ litre (l)}$
$1 \text{ cm}^3 = 1 \text{ millilitre (ml)}$

vulgar fractions

Vulgar fractions are the ordinary common fractions with a numerator and a denominator like
$\frac{1}{2}, \frac{4}{5}, \frac{9}{10}, \frac{2}{3}$.
If you have forgotten about these look up **fractions**.

weight

Heaviness. We use balances or scales to find out how heavy something is. We use bathroom scales to weigh ourselves. In the post office they use letter scales to weigh our letters. Shopkeepers weigh our fruit and vegetables. In some Maths books they use the word mass where you might expect to see weight. They may say, 'Measure the mass' not 'Find the weight'. Look up **mass** if you need to know about this. The tables of measurements you need are the same. For everyday use the units of mass are used for weight.

Metric units of mass

1000 milligrams (mg) = 1 gram (g)
1000 grams = 1 kilogram (kg)
1000 kilograms = 1 tonne
We might sometimes need
100 grams = 1 hectogram
10 hectograms = 1 kilogram (kg)
1 kilogram is about 2·2 lb

Imperial units of mass

16 ounces (oz) = 1 pound (lb)
14 pounds (lb) = 1 stone
112 pounds   = 1 hundredweight (cwt)
20 cwt   = 1 ton
1 lb is about 0·45 kg

yard

An old style measure of length.

12 inches (in) = 1 foot (ft)
3 feet   = 1 yard (yd)
1760 yd   = 1 mile
1 yard   = 36 inches
1 metre is just over 39 inches.
1 yard is about 8 cm less than a metre.
(1 inch is about $2\frac{1}{2}$ cm)

zero

The sign for zero is 0.
We call it nought.
If we talk about the temperature being 'below zero' we mean it is below freezing point. It is below 0°C. (0 degrees on the Celsius or centigrade scale.)

There is a section about **noughts** in this book which might interest you.